DEFERENCE TO DOUBT

DEFERENCE TO DOUBT

A Young Man's Quest for Religious Identity
in First Century Judea

» HERMAN M. VAN PRAAG «

Translated from the Dutch by
Rosalind Buck

Foreword by
Robert Haim Belmaker, MD

URIM PUBLICATIONS
Jerusalem • New York

Deference to Doubt:
A Young Man's Quest for Religious Identity
in First Century Judea

Professor Herman M. van Praag

Translated from the Dutch by Rosalind Buck
Foreword by Robert Haim Belmaker, MD

This publication has been made possible
with financial support from
the Dutch Foundation for Literature.

N ederlands
letterenfonds
dutch foundation
for literature

Typeset by Ariel Walden

Printed in Israel

First Edition

ISBN 978-1-60280-370-1

Urim Publications
P.O. Box 52287
Jerusalem 9152102
Israel

www.UrimPublications.com

Library of Congress Cataloging-in-Publication Data in progress.

I said to myself:
All this I tested by wisdom and I said,
"I am determined to be wise"
    – but this was beyond me.

Ecclesiastes 7:23, 26

To my wife and greatest treasure

To the Preacher

CONTENTS

Contents

FOREWORD

It is my pleasure to write a foreword to this English version of *Slecht zicht: Een hommage aan de twijfel* ("Dimmed View: An Hommage to Doubt") now published as "Deference to Doubt: A Young Man's Quest for Religious Identity in First Century Judea." Herman van Praag has been my colleague, scientific collaborator and friend for 45 years. He survived the Holocaust in Holland as an adolescent and always dreamed of making Aliya to live in Israel. As bright as he was, numerous opportunities always presented themselves in Europe and the USA and led to his having an illustrious international career in the burgeoning field of psychopharmacology.

He was one of the first scientists in the world to study the mechanism of action of antidepressants and other compounds for psychiatric illness. He was an early formulator of the "serotonin hypothesis of depression." He pioneered the rigorous scientific method in psychiatry, including empirical rating scales and examination of body fluids of patients with depression. In particular he championed the concept that scientists must always have a testable hypothesis, also in the sphere of psychiatric research. Each of his studies was a pearl of the scientific method with a hypothesis, a methodology, results and relevant conclusions. He was never a reductionist or a believer that science implies certainty, that diagnosis implies causation and especially not mono-causation.

All through the years of his hundreds of scientific studies and his promotion through the ranks to full Professor of Psychiatry and Chairman of Psychiatry in Utrecht, Holland and then at Albert Einstein College of Medicine in New York, he always nurtured another side of himself. He always believed that there was more to mankind than the material alone, that humans have spiritual yearnings and spiritual doubt that deserve attention. He did not say that this spiritual component was necessarily the realm of psychiatry and if I understand him correctly I think he feels that it is above psychiatry and perhaps more important than psychiatry.

His friends, his colleagues, and his intellectual dialogue have always been worldwide but he has never denied, forgotten, downplayed, or left behind his deep Jewish roots. His new book sheds interesting light both on Herman van Praag as a person whom I have known so long and also provides insights that I believe are of universal value.

This book was originally written in Dutch and this English version comes out now on the occasion of the meeting of the World Psychiatric Association Congress on Psychiatry, Religion and Spirituality December 1–4, 2019 in Jerusalem, Israel, a city that he has always loved and in which he has spent two academic sabbaticals. Herman Van Praag never felt that his love of Jerusalem is controversial or in any way conflicts with his universal contributions in science and psychiatry. He founded the World Psychiatric Association Section on Religion and Psychiatry and is the recipient of the Founders award of this organization.

Robert Haim Belmaker, MD
Modiin, Israel 2019

*

INTRODUCTION

Therefore I prayed, and understanding was given me; I called
on God, and the spirit of wisdom came to me. I preferred her
to sceptres and thrones and I accounted wealth as nothing in
comparison with her . . . I chose to have her rather than light,
because her radiance never ceases.

The Wisdom of Solomon 7:7–8

A. EXPLANATION

What is this book about? A question one generally asks oneself
before taking up a contemplative book. In this case, the answer
is: it is about doubt. The main character in this book is a young
Judean named Amos. He asks questions and, receiving answers
that he often finds unsatisfactory, he continues to ask. Doubt
persists, however. He finds that he must live with it. Perhaps
doubt is an essential and inevitable component of life, he muses.

Why did I dedicate this book to the Preacher? Above all
because of my admiration for him as the author of Ecclesiastes. This bible book is named in Hebrew "Koheleth," while in
Christian tradition the Greek rendering, "Ecclesiastes" – found
in the Septuagint – is used. Koheleth belongs to the so called
Wisdom Literature, a collection of non-canonical writings, the
author of which is purported to be King Solomon. Ecclesiastes
is a high point in Wisdom Literature. It is a profound work and,

moreover, a literary masterpiece, abundantly demonstrating the king's wisdom and artistry.[1]

The way I read this book, it is pervaded with doubt. Certainty, says the Preacher, is not given to man. It stresses the inadequacy of human comprehension, in understanding God's intentions and motives, for grasping the meaning of life. The quest for that understanding is eternal. "I applied my heart to know wisdom and to see the business that is done on earth . . . man cannot find out the work that is done under the sun. Though a man labor to seek it out, yet he shall not find it."[2] The famous first few words of the writing are typical. In the King James version, the translation is, "Vanity of vanities, sayeth the Preacher, Vanity of vanities!" The term vain is used in the sense of useless, transient, futile, not the sense of conceit. It is the translation of the Hebrew word *hèbèl*, which means breath.

The Christian Standard Bible leaves out the word "vanity" and translates the text thus:[3] "Absolute futility," says the Teacher. "Absolute futility. Everything is futile."

The International Standard Version makes of it this: "Utterly pointless," says the Teacher. "Absolutely pointless." That approaches the concept of *hèbèl* more closely, but the translator follows it with, "It is all meaningless." That, in my view, misses the mark. A breath is fleeting, not futile or meaningless; it is essential for life.

Nonetheless, notions such as futile, transient and fleeting fail to grasp what, in my view, the Preacher essentially wants to convey: not the futility, but the relativity of all human endeavour. He follows the famous opening words with the lamentation:[4]

> What does man gain by all the trial at which he toils under the sun?

And he concludes:[5]

> What has been is what will be, and what has been done is what will be done, and there is nothing new under the sun.

Fig. 1 Max Weber. *The Talmudists*, 1934

Study and discussion of the holy scriptures has traditionally been a core element of Judaism, centred on the yeshiva, the Jewish school. Here, views were exchanged, no judgements were passed *ex cathedra*. The Talmud literally speaks volumes: a triumph of dialectics over religious dogma.

And yet, the Preacher says, "the eye is not satisfied with seeing, nor the ear filled with hearing."[6]

I interpret this as a call to keep seeking answers to key questions that life raises, such as: "What is the meaning of my life?" "Was I created for a purpose, or merely by chance"[7] and, in the first instance, "What is then the purpose and who determined it? I, myself? And if not, then who?"

Do not expect any definite answers, the Preacher appears to say, but keep searching. Maintain the debate. With yourself and with others. Keep the dialogue going. Do not seek refuge in false assurances, in dogmatic theology. Embrace dialectics, your whole life through. The Preacher concludes his quest with the words:[8]

> Behold, this is what I found, says the Preacher, while adding one thing to another to find the scheme of things –
> Which my soul has sought repeatedly, but I have not found . . . God made man upright, but they have sought out many schemes.

It is, though, those very illusions that are the spice of life, I might add.

There is another reason why I am paying tribute to the Preacher, though: in him I recognize a kindred spirit, albeit with an opposing valence. Scepticism and doubt lead, in the Preacher's eyes, to defeatism, to resignation, while they spur me on to pursue the seemingly endless quest. Doubt can be exhausting, but it can also be exhilarating.

The Preacher and I are antipodean kindred spirits.

The young Judean who plays the main part in this book has taken my words to heart. He recounts his trials and tribulations. He speaks in his own right, but in his views I often recognize my own. Not surprisingly. After all, I begot him myself.

B. STRUCTURE

Amos the young Judean tells of an intellectual and spiritual odyssey. He is in search of who he is, wishes to become and, ultimately, wishes to be. Amos lives in the first half of the first century. He was born shortly after the death of King Herod I in the year 4 BCE. Herod's successor in Judea, Archelaus, one of his sons, was deposed by the Roman emperor in 6 CE for mismanagement. Judea came under the direct rule of Rome. Politically, the country was bitterly divided. "Hawks," bent on liberating themselves from Roman domination by force, and "doves" seeking accommodation with the Romans.

At a social level, wide gaps appeared, gaps between poor and rich, city folk and country folk, the educated and the illiterate, between more or less Hellenized Jews and traditional Jews. Things are not much different from a religious perspective. Division abounds. Amos does not know which way to turn.

C. BACKGROUND HISTORY

Internal tensions were not a new phenomenon for this Jewish country. They had been around, in fact, since the very beginning. After the death of King Solomon, they mounted so far that the country was literally torn in two and, after years of civil war, fractured into two parts: the northern state of Israel, where ten of the twelve tribes had settled, and the southern state of Judea, homeland to Benjamin and Juda's tribes (928 BCE).

In 722 BCE, the state of Israel was destroyed by the Assyrians, its people removed and replaced by heathen groups from other parts of the Syrian Empire. The land disappeared from history. Two centuries later, Judea rebelled against the Babylonian Empire (586 BCE). The elite of the population was deported to Babylon. Fifty years later, when the Persians vanquished the Babylonians, the exiles were able to return to Judea and rebuild the country, including the Temple (539 BCE). Judea remained preserved, but became a vassal of the Persian Empire until this, in its turn, was conquered by Alexander the Great (333 BCE).

After that, Judea answered to two Greek royal houses founded by Ptolemy and Seleucus, two of Alexander's former generals. The Maccabean revolt, led by Judas, a member of the house of Hasmon, put an end to that. Judas' warlike character earned him the name Maccabeus (derived from the Hebrew word for hammer). Judea once again became an independent kingdom, a throne occupied by the descendants of the leaders of that revolt, the Hasmonean Kings (142–63 BCE). Members of the Orthodox Jewish community, the Chassideans, also took part in the revolt. For them, it was more about religious than national liberty. They were disappointed, however. In addition to the kingship, the Hasmoneans also appropriated the High Priesthood. A wrongful act. Only descendants of the line of Aaron/Zadok were permitted to lay claim to this office.

The combination of king/high priest held no blessing. Priestly obligations were shirked. The Chassideans became increasingly frustrated and retreated into their trusted bastion: the Holy Scriptures. Some of these were inspired by a preacher, whom they came to call the Teacher of Righteousness. His followers were called the Essenes, probably a bastardisation of the Hebrew Zeduqi, the descendants of Zadok.

Most Essenes continued living in towns and villages. The ultra-orthodox amongst them withdrew entirely from society and settled in Qumran, where they formed a proto-monastic community. The discovery of the Dead Sea Scrolls provided a wealth of knowledge on the way of life and the views of the Qumran community.

The Romans put an end to the maladministration of the Hasmonean kings and placed Judea under the direct authority of Rome (63–37 BCE). In 37 BCE, it pleased the emperor to allocate the throne of Judea to Herod (37–4 BCE). His son Archelaus succeeded him, but was given a lesser title, that of "ethnarch." As already mentioned, he was deposed by the Romans in the year 6 CE for maladministration. Judah returned to the direct authority of Rome. That meant tax collection for the emperor and, consequently, a census. Jews paying taxes for the Temple in Jerusalem were loath to give money for building heathen temples in Rome. The census, too, engendered disgust. The procedure symbolized the fact that the people belonged to the emperor, while the Jewish people believed themselves to be the Lord's people.

A revolt broke out, led by Judas the Galilean and Zadok the Priest. They were at the front of a group of staunch nationalists, bent on liberating themselves from the Roman yoke with violence. Initially, this was a rather incohesive group. When the war against the Romans approached (67–70 CE), however, it really structured itself into what might be called a party, that of the zealots.

The rebellion that broke out after the death of Archelaus was mercilessly crushed by Varus, the Roman governor of Syria. Thousands of rebels were crucified and many were taken into slavery.

Fear combined with hopeful expectation now characterized the atmosphere in the country. Fear that the Lord had withdrawn His protective hand from His people or was about to do so. And hope and expectation that the coming of the Messiah was near or that he was already in their midst. The end times must be approaching; a bright future lay in the offing, at least to those who had shown timely remorse and improved their lives.

Judea is in turmoil. The social cohesion is breaking down. Amos can no longer see the wood for the trees. He has lost his way.

D. CONTENT

Amos asks his father for advice. His father counsels him to go and listen to a number of spiritual leaders. This he does. He does not only listen, though. He expresses criticism, crossing swords with them. He talks with a Pharisee, a proto-rabbi. He talks with a priest, a member of a high-priestly family, and then with a staunch nationalist – a zealot – eager to resist the Roman occupiers with violence. He then travels into the desert and stays for a while in Qumran, on the north-western shores of the Dead Sea, with a group of pietistic Jews who oppose "Jerusalem," the Judaism that, at the time, counted as normative. They see themselves as God's chosen people, the "Children of the Light," the "New Israel." On his way back to Judea, he meets, in succession, Yochanan (John) the Baptist and Joshua of Nazareth, better known as Jesus of Nazareth. He gains the latter's confidence, engaging him in extremely personal discussions.

Finally, his father enables him to undertake a voyage to Egypt, to meet Philo in Alexandria. This philosopher exegete is a connoisseur of both biblical literature and the writings of the Greek philosophers. He is attempting to bridge the two realms of thought and so develop a Hellenistically-tinted Judaism. A hybrid of Jewish and Greek ideology.

What is discussed in these dialogues? Much, including the image people make for themselves of the Lord; the question of whether death is the end of the journey or the beginning of a new one; whether we are subject to predestination or self-ordination; whether an apocalypse does indeed threaten; whether the extreme dualism that divides humanity into the undefiled and the black sheep, is a correct interpretation of God's vision; how the synagogue relates to the Temple; whether the Oral Torah – our traditions – was given by God or produced by man; whether Jesus is, indeed 'God's suffering servant,' the figure of whom Isaiah had spoken,[9] why he behaved so provocatively, seeking death, as it were; and whether the concept of Logos, which Philo introduced into our teachings is a step towards blasphemy and his way of Bible exegesis more of a reinterpretation than an explanation.

On his return, Amos recounts his experiences to his father. He talks about how he wants to structure his life and give his "inner self" an individual face. That face will be pervaded with doubt. Of that he is certain.

E. CHARACTER

Is this a typically Jewish book? Yes and no. Yes, because it is set in old Judea and the identity of the author clearly shows through. No, because the book is certainly not aimed exclusively at Jewish readers. So saying, it is a theistic book. It is aimed at those who need to add a vertical dimension to their life and seek that within a monotheistic framework. In Amos' time, there was only one such framework available: Judaism. Many of the discussion points are not of a sectarian nature, not typically Jewish, but have a more general tenor. Some are relevant for religious people, but no less for thinking secular people.

In short, this book is aimed at those who, like the writer, enjoy dialogue and are interested in questions and ideas that elevate man above the horizontal level of the everyday. Questions such as: Who am I? Who do I want to be? Why am I here and how can I give meaning to that "being here"?

This foreword would be incomplete without a word of sincere thanks to Dinie and Hans Pol. They have been an indispensable administrative aid in creating this book.

I would also like extend my thanks to the English translator Rosalind Buck and to the Dutch Literature Foundation for their subsidy, which helped make the translation of this book possible.

The biblical quotes in English are taken from The New International Version of the Bible.

Comme vn Iuif tenant son fils repoussa
Iesus-Christ, qui se vouloit reposer de-
uant sa porte & fut faict errant.

Comme le Iuif errant rencontra deux
Gentilhommes françois ces iours passez
au pres Chaalons.

Fig. 2 The Wandering Jew.

For centuries, this was an archetypical figure in anti-Semitic mythology.
He is said to have mocked Jesus on his way to the cross and, as punishment,
to have been doomed to wander, homeless, until judgement day.
From: H. Schreckenberg (1996). *The Jews in Christian art. An illustrated
history*. London SCM Press.

To me, the wandering Jew is actually the opposite symbol: The prototype
of what the Jew should be – anti-dogmatic, curious, always in search of new
horizons, someone following in the footsteps of Abraham.

CHAPTER 1

THE QUESTION: WHO AM I AND WHO DO I WANT TO BE?

And, above all: ask questions! Do not content yourself with the obvious answers. Keep asking questions.

For what man is he that can know the counsel of God? Or who can think what the will of the Lord is? For the thoughts of mortal men are miserable, and our devices are but uncertain.

The Wisdom of Solomon 9:13–14

A. PROFILE

My name is Amos. I'm a seeker and a doubter, a combination that makes my life interesting, but not easy. So what am I seeking? Who I want to be. I know who I *am*. An ordinary young man. Nearly twenty-five years old, actually. I was born of a Jewish mother shortly after the death of King Herod[10] and circumcised on my eighth day. I live in Jerusalem. Formally speaking, then, I am a Jew. But that's the 'outside.' What's the 'inside' of a Jew like? What should he think, believe and do to be an authentic Jew? What is his image of God? What are his thoughts on self-determination, on free will? Does he believe death is the end of the journey or the beginning of a new one? That we're here by chance or with a purpose and, if the latter be true, then what is that purpose and by whom is it decided? I have endless questions, but no answers. I can't resign myself to such a situation. I want to give form to my "inner self."

Friends of mine have said, "Don't bother your head about it. You belong to a people that, for many years, has shared joys and sorrows. That common history determines your identity." "We are what we remember," one of them remarked.[11] "But that's only half the truth, I replied, "In fact, it's less than half, in my opinion. The fundamental principles of the Teachings Moses gave us: that's where the building bricks of our identity lie. I want to learn to know and understand them."

So where did that need come from? I don't know. It may hark back to a horrible period in my still short life. When King Herod died, his son Archelaus became the ruler of Judea. There were protests against his regime.[12] I took part and was arrested, imprisoned. The guards treated me terribly, repeatedly threatening me with death. That episode may have reinforced my need to profile myself as a Jew, but I'll draw a veil over the rest.

B. CIRCUMSTANCES

The era in which I live doesn't help. Our society is chaotic and seemingly held together no better than loose sand, on all fronts, but particularly in politics. Archelaus, the tetrarch, behaved so badly that he was deposed by the Roman emperor and, ever since, we've been under the direct authority of Rome. The emperor is represented by a procurator. And where did this official set himself up? Not in our beloved capital, Jerusalem, but in Caesarea, a town King Herod recently established to the further glory of his patron, Caesar, adding insult to injury.

We're bitterly divided over what attitude we should take to our oppressors. At one extreme there are those who do their utmost to accommodate the Roman government, up to and including collaboration. They call themselves the Freedom Party. At the other end are the zealots, extreme nationalists who reject any idea of conciliation with the Romans. They want to drive them out of the country and are spoiling for war. A crazy idea: a dwarf against the giant. They're counting on support from the Lord, but the time when the Lord took us directly by the hand is long past. Now, we're standing on our own two feet. Between those two extremes – accommodation or collaboration and resistance – lies a legion of nuances. Everyone wants to have their say, whether they know what they're talking about or not.

Things are not much better on the religious front. Division all around. The people have long since forgotten how to speak with one voice. There are power games being played. The priests are struggling madly to consolidate their waning authority, clinging like grim death to the dictate that the Temple and ritual sacrifices are essential to our worship of the Lord. Their influence has ebbed. A new elite has emerged, gaining substantial popularity. This consists of our teachers, the Rabbis, who are experts in the Mosaic laws. They discuss them with us, explain them, and teach us how to apply them in daily life. They're called Pharisees, separatists, and they believe the Law should be strictly observed. Particularly the cleanliness laws: not just by priests, but by all Jews, at home, and within the family. Many of them are rigid in their views, distancing themselves from ordinary people, who are often less conscientious in such matters.

The Pharisees constitute a far from homogeneous group, too. There are hair-splitters and nit-pickers among them, unwilling to make the slightest compromise, but also more liberal minds. These take the spirit of the Law more seriously than the letter. They're prepared to make concessions and listen to the 'unauthorized,' those less versed in our Teachings. Again: between those extremes are many nuances. Who, in God's name, should you believe?

And then there are those seen by the pious amongst us as 'defectors' and by rather freer spirits as apples that have fallen too far from the tree. They're fascinated by everything the Greek culture has to offer. They immerse themselves in it – they Hellenize – and make so many religious concessions that the original law is barely recognizable. For strictly observant Jews this is unbearable. They foresee it bringing down the wrath of the Lord on our people. In their opinion, a doom scenario is looming. Apocalyptic preachers are taking advantage of this. They believe the end time is nigh, but will be preceded by a terrible final battle. In Qumran lives yet another community, which feels that, nowadays, the practice of Judaism is perverted to the core. They see themselves as the "new Israel." Finally, a Hellenized Judaism seems to be developing in the diaspora, a kind of hybrid of Moses' teachings and Greek philosophy. It all makes me giddy!

Deep social rifts have also formed. Primarily between poor and rich. Over the past few years, in Judea, an upper class has emerged made up of landowners. They mostly live in town and have had the opportunity to cultivate themselves intellectually. They're not far removed from the old elite, members of high-priestly families and folk, related or closely connected to members of our former royal houses: the House of Hasmon and the House of Herod. Not uncommonly, their prosperity is due, in part, to these relations.[13]

Many of the poor are dependent on the generosity of this financial elite, which is woefully lacking, and they are now barely able to pay the taxes imposed by Rome. Not infrequently, they are obliged to sell themselves as slaves to pay off their debts. The rich show little compassion for the poor. They generally look down on the wretches. The Sanhedrin[14] shows far too little concern for their plight, too. It's a moral fiasco for a people that's supposedly walking in the footsteps of the Lord.

The wealthy are fond of not only money, but also power and prestige and the power is in Rome's hands. It's primarily this group that has started behaving in a 'Roman' fashion, eagerly participating in Roman cultural life. To me, that's tragicomic. Comic because they're so clearly not Romans. Tragic because they will never be accepted as such. They're fake Romans.

Our people is splintered. We're like a puzzle whose pieces

no longer fit together. That scares me. It's eroding our social capital. People now have too little interest in one another, too little trust in and too little respect for our own leaders. We're only interested in ourselves, a trend that leads to a loss of social cohesion. In time, that process can lead to the dissolution of a society.

Dissolution of the only Jewish country in the world. It doesn't bear thinking about! Is the people the Lord commanded to forge a path to a more humane society busy writing itself out of history? That would be disastrous. We've still trodden so little of that path.

This situation not only strikes fear in me, it confuses me. How can I distil a Jewish identity from this near chaos? What attitude should a Judean adopt towards Roman authority and the Hellenistic culture? What's the hallmark of an authentic Jew? Which choices should I make? Should I be impartial instead and color my own spiritual existence, shaping it with my own 'hands' and organizing my thinking in such a way that I feel comfortable? As I already mentioned, the term Jew is, in itself, no more than a label. What lies behind it? Which elements of that philosophy of life are essential for my own life?

I discussed these problems with my father, a highly-cultured, wise man. A true mentor for me. He said, "I can't, no, I won't answer your questions. Only you can find an answer to them."

"What do you advise me to do, Father?" I asked. He patted me on the shoulder. "Explore the 'market,' son, absorb more detailed knowledge of everything that's for sale in the spiritual field, think about it and form your own opinion. And, above all: ask questions. Don't be content with obvious answers. Keep questioning. Contradict if you don't agree with the answer. Ask for explanation if you don't understand an answer. Don't be overawed by authority, by religious or social status. It's sometimes no more than a veneer. It has a lovely shine, but it's wafer thin. Neither must you let yourself be overawed by knowledge, factual knowledge. For questions such as yours, there often isn't enough knowledge available. Here, in particular, is where your heart has to speak.

Be impressed, open your mind where you feel there is understanding, compassion and wisdom. The important thing is to shape your identity and therefore, in essence, give your life meaning. Life becomes meaningful when you attempt to make your identity real, to give it substance. Meaning has more to do with the heart than the head. Bear that in mind. Go forth, *lech lecha* [Hebrew]."[15]

I followed my father's advice. It became a journey full of clashes. A journey that was to be open-ended. What follows here is an account of my experiences.

CHAPTER 2

JACOB, A PHARISEE

I am a believer and, therefore, I doubt.

It was he who created humankind in the beginning, and he left them in the power of their own free choice . . . Before each person are life and death, and whichever one chooses will be given.

Ben Sira 15:14, 27

A. WHAT AM I SEEKING?

My first visit was to Jacob, a man whose lessons I had followed and enjoyed at the synagogue. He was clearly a pious man. After all, he counted himself amongst the Pharisees, a group that is highly versed in the laws of Moses, applies them rigorously and expects us to do likewise.

Jacob was devout, but mild in his judgement of others, certainly no intolerant nit-picker like some of his spiritual peers. He was able to listen to his pupils and took them seriously. A born teacher.

I knocked at his house. He opened the door himself, regarding me with a slightly bemused look. "Remind me who you are."

"I'm Amos."

"How silly of me not to recognize you immediately," he laughed. "Welcome. I remember now. You were a very good pupil, asking questions, thinking things through."

"I'm glad you thought so."

He sat down at the table and indicated the chair opposite. "Take a seat, my boy. So, what are you up to now? What are you doing here?"

"Not much, Jacob, just hanging around, still living with my parents."

"Are you looking for work?"

"No, that's not it. I'm trying to find myself, my identity, the person I want to become. I feel like a random piece of matter that still has to be shaped into a recognizable individual."

Jacob looked up in surprise. "Well, that must be a fascinating quest, but what's it got to do with me? I can't shape that 'piece of matter,' as you describe yourself. You'll have to do that yourself. A teacher provides building blocks and the pupil builds."

"I understand that Jacob, but it's actually building blocks that I'm after, answers to questions I'm wrestling with. I'm at a cross-roads and I don't know which way to go."

Jacob sighed. "Okay, then, fire away," he smiled, "But don't make it too difficult for me. First, though, I have a question for you. You know I insist on first defining the concept to be discussed. So, what do you understand by identity?"

"I thought that's what you'd ask me. That concept represents the core of who I am. To put it poetically: it's my personal stamp, my hallmark, the signature at the bottom of what I call my personality."

I paused for a moment. "And your second question will be: So what's personality? My answer is simple: "It's the sum of all the characteristics that make me into a recognizable, unique individual."

"Well put," nodded Jacob, "But, again, by definition, your identity is your business. There's nothing I can contribute."

"With your permission, Master, you're mistaken. A teacher can be an example, a role model in his way of thinking, in his approach to life. His insights, his attitude to life may be able to clarify problems with which his pupils are struggling."

Jacob shook his head. "You haven't changed; you always have

Fig. 3 Remains of a synagogue from the 3rd–2nd century CE in Capernaum (Kfar Nahum) on the northern coast of the Sea of Galilee.
From: Ben Gurion, D. (Ed) (1974). *The Jews in their land*. London: Aldus Books.

The Pharisees – proto-rabbis – founded houses of learning where the Torah was studied and the people were taught how to put God's guidelines into practice. These houses of learning developed into places of worship, the precursors of the synagogues.

to have the last word. But never mind, these are sensible words. All right, then, let's begin."

B.   DOES GOD EXIST?

I fidgeted restlessly on my chair.

"Out with it, young man," Jacob urged,

"I hope I haven't already annoyed you with my first question."

"I don't easily get angry, you know that."

"Well, does the Lord really exist?" I mumbled.

Jacob drummed his fingers on the table. Evidently, this was not a question he'd expected from one of his pupils. He sighed. "Before I answer your question, I have a counter question. As you know, we Jews are good at that. Question and counter question. It spices up the discussion. Which figure in the Bible appeals most to your imagination?"

"One figure?"

"Yes."

"Abraham. Now that's a man I admire. He was seized by an idea. There is only one God, he imagined. Other gods, even family gods, are idols, impotent fancies, fabrications. That one God commanded him to go forth: *lech lecha* (Hebrew).[52] Where to? It's unclear; into the unknown. Why? Unclear; a vague and improbable suggestion. He was offered the perspective of becoming the founding father of a great nation.[53] He went forth, leaving everything behind him: culture, possessions. He uprooted himself. He believed in the task; felt he was up to it. Dared to break away from the mainstream."

Jacob interrupted me: "He trusted in the Lord. He believed in Him. That was what gave him the strength."

I was getting in the swing of things. I like discussion; it invigorates me. With a slight air of challenge, I replied, "I agree, Teacher-Rabbi, if I may call you that?"

"You may, my boy."

"I agree, Rabbi, but you haven't answered my question: Does the Lord exist?"

His answer was decisive. "He exists and I suspect that your next question will be, 'How do you know?' So I'll answer you straight away. He exists if you believe in Him. The Lord Himself already answered your question. He taught us that we were created to bear witness to Him."[54]

"But that's not proof. You can bear witness to something that doesn't actually exist."

"You're bearing witness to something that exists for you. That 'something' may not exist for anyone else, because it can't be detected with the senses. But you perceive that 'something,' so it exists, for you. By that 'something' I mean the Lord, you understand."

"But, surely, it could be a case of *trompe-l'oeil*, an optical illusion. The Lord appears to be there but is, in fact, a figment of our own imagination."

I was enjoying the discussion. Jacob was plainly enjoying it less. "No, it's not an optical illusion," he retorted. "Think of Moses' core statement: 'choose life'[55] . . . life is created. Creation assumes a Creator. If a man realizes this with his mind, and experiences it with his feelings, then he draws near to the Lord. The Lord is no mirage. He exists in you, and thanks to you.

Don't underestimate imagination, Amos. It's a force no less essential to our existence than the power of thought. It reveals to us realities behind the perceptible reality, the existence of which we can only suspect."[56]

I was surprised, having expected a different, far more positive answer. "Is the Lord no more than the personal perception, then; does He disappear if I disappear? Is that not too scant an image of God? I need a superhuman mentor, a Super Moses, a father figure, who will be there as long as the world exists and even thereafter.

Years ago, I heard a story that illustrates what I mean. I've always remembered it, Rabbi. It goes like this. A crowd of people is gathered on the coast, watching a boat leaving port. A little boy is standing, waving as hard as he can. A bystander asks why he's doing that. 'I'm waving so the captain can see me and wave back.' 'But the boat is so far off and there are so many people here,' replies the man. 'What makes you think the captain will see you?' 'Because the captain of the ship is my father,' says the boy. 'He will look out for me and manage to find me.'"[57]

Jacob sighed. "An apt story, indeed. I understand you. You're not alone in that. Let that image of God guide you. Only the Lord himself knows if He exists outside the imagination of our people. People can only guess. It remains a mystery. It's better that way. Mysteries are essential ingredients in our existence. They encourage us to reflect."

There was a moment of silence. "You know, you amaze me, Rabbi, and that's putting it mildly. You never expressed yourself like that in the classroom."

"No, I didn't. In my public lessons, I've always kept to the views of normative Judaism. In those views, the Lord exists axiomatically. No discussion. He is the Creator of everything that exists and He will exist for all eternity; full stop.

Over the years, though, I've found that doctrine increasingly less appealing. Believing in God has become less a question of blindly accepting pre-digested, imposed doctrines and more a matter of experiencing. The perception of a creating, guiding Authority above man has gained more and more substance and meaning. For me, it's become the best 'proof' of the existence of a Being that, in essence, will always remain the ultimate abstraction: present, but forever veiled in impenetrable mists.

This emphasis on experience and perception is no admission of weakness. On the contrary. I'll give you what I feel is a striking analogy: I love my wife dearly. That's how I perceive it. I can't prove it and I have no need of proof. For me, the perception is convincing proof."

"So, is your belief anchored solely in your inner perceptions?"

"No, Amos, reason is involved, too. I can't imagine that the earth, initially 'without form and void,'[58] has become what it is now by pure chance. To explain that, I introduce ideas into my life, the Lord is both perception and idea."

"You deviate quite substantially from the way we Jews are supposed to think. In the circles you move in, are you accepted or do you keep your mouth shut?"

"No, I open my mouth, not too wide but wide enough for many of my colleagues to think of me as a renegade and, for the ultra-pious amongst them, an apostate. Worse still: a denier of God."

"That must hurt, Jacob."

"Yes, it does, but that's no reason to change my mind. I simply perceive the world as I perceive it. And I let that be known. I don't flatter myself with the idea that my beliefs have plumbed the depths of my emotional life. That's what it comes down to. I haven't gotten bogged down in intellectual nit-picking, something at which many of my colleagues excel these days. Our people have always advocated dialogue: asking questions, sowing doubt, debating. From that point of view, I don't deviate from the principles of our philosophy of life. I'm actually attempting to honor them."

"Do you have any allies?"

"Not that I know of. There are people who are willing to listen to me. The Pharisee community explores reform. It doesn't consist solely of the ultra-devout; it also includes religious 'doves' and all variations in between. We have no supreme leader who has the last word, either. The 'doves' listen to me and respond but don't judge. It wouldn't surprise me to find there are more who think as I do, but keep quiet out of a sense of understandable self-interest."

I wasn't sure what to say and Jacob could tell.

"Remember, Amos, you don't have to share my opinion. I'm averse to any kind of belief imposed from above. Seek your own way heavenwards. Belief is a personal affair. Impersonal belief is a form of sanctimoniousness."

He was quiet. I was quiet. For several minutes, or so it seemed. Finally, I mumbled, "Thank you for your forthrightness."

"Thank you for engendering trust in me," he replied. Not many people manage to do that."

C. IS LIFE FINITE?

I shifted my chair slightly towards the table at which Jacob was sitting. "There are a number of other things I'd like to ask," I continued, without waiting for his answer. "These days, Rabbi, I hear so much talk of the end time. They say it's approaching. The dead will be resurrected, summoned before a heavenly court to be judged for their deeds here on earth. Sinners will be punished, the righteous rewarded. Everlasting punishment and reward apparently. There is even talk of a terrible final battle preceding the end time. I'm sure you know all about it. I find such thoughts chilling."

"I can imagine, young man, but remember that the end time is also supposed to finish in triumph. They say a new world, an *Olam Haba* (Hebrew), will come. A world quite different from this, a kind of return to paradise in which time has made way for eternity, where only those men dwell whom the Lord has deemed 'righteous.'"

"Yes, yes, Rabbi, I'm familiar with all those notions, but for me they raise as many questions. Does that *Olam Haba* actually exist? Does it already exist now, or will it exist at some point? If the new world doesn't yet exist, then where are all the so-called dead in the meantime? If that *Olam Haba* does exist now, then when will the final judgement take place? One time only, in the end time? Or now already and with some regularity, as the flow of the dead is continuous? And then there's the key question: assuming that death is not irrevocable, then what survives? Only the soul? Or will the body also be brought back to life?"

"Questions, questions and more questions. I can't give you any answers, Amos. No one can. I'm struggling with this myself.

Many of my spiritual colleagues do have strong views on it, though: the *Olam Haba* does exist; death doesn't mean the end of life. The body dies; the *nefesh* (Hebrew) – the breath of life – leaves. The *neshama* (Hebrew) – the soul – escapes that fate and lives on; for eternity."

"All souls."

"Yes, but their fates are said to differ. The Lord takes to him those of the righteous. As you said, these have a bright future. The souls of incorrigible sinners disappear into the underworld, the *Sheol* (Hebr.), for good, or so they say. To put it irreverently, good riddance to bad rubbish."[59]

"If I hear you correctly, Rabbi, then your viewpoint is more one of, 'I reject those ideas' than 'I don't know.'"

"You read me well, Amos; at least partly. My intellect won't accept this. A new world filled with souls? Why would the Lord want that? He formed man from dust and then breathed the breath of life into his nostrils,[60] bringing the dead dust to life. Death, by definition, means the departure of the breath of life. End of story. What's more, the soul can't be seen as a kind of thing that enters the body and then, when the time comes, leaves it again. The soul has no spatial limits. It's a kind of fluid that permeates our entire being, making us into a recognizable individual. It's like the precious gem you were talking about: your hallmark, the signature at the bottom of who you are. It's an essential ingredient of our existence. There's no body without the soul and no soul without its body. They're inextricably bound together.

What's more, according to Moses, the Lord never talked about a coming world, or an immortal soul. That's got to mean something. Let's face it, the topic was important enough. That, too, shows that man himself came up with these ideas about immortality."

"Was there a point to that?"

"Well of course. They fulfil a function, don't you see? Stay on the straight and narrow path, people, then everything will turn out right in the end. If you stray from that path, then things will go badly for you. A useful rather than an uplifting idea. You tread the straight and narrow path because it does you good; you avoid the wrong way because straying onto that path gives you a feeling of unease. That's the ideal, but daily practice, so it seems, is problematic. The Lord had promised to reward good behavior and punish unacceptable behavior. Many people thought that was in a material sense, and in our world. But too often, in day-to-day reality, that proved not to be the case. The mental image of the *Olam Haba* bade solace. Anyone who doesn't receive what they deserve in this world will get their desserts in the next. That idea generates hope."

"So, it's simply palliative, in other words."

That sounded sarcastic but, as usual, Jacob answered amiably, "You could say that, but such palliative measures are indispensable, even for religious teachers."

"Correct me if I'm wrong, Rabbi, but you're actually rejecting the whole philosophy of immortality as speculative."

"No, Amos, that's not what I mean. So far, I've been letting my reason speak. My reason doubts this, but my heart speaks another language. It says, 'Jacob your soul lives on.' When you die, it's the *nefesh* – God's breath that woke the dead dust to life – that disappears, not the *neshama*, our soul. The Lord gave us the *nefesh*. That's a gift of God, but it's not personal. On the other hand, each of us actually builds up the *neshama* during our lifetime. With our own hands, in a manner of speaking. I can't believe such a gem disappears into the dustbin on death. The Lord wouldn't allow that to happen. Deep in my heart, I'm certain of that."

"Now you're contradicting yourself, Jacob. You don't know what death will bring and yet you're certain the soul survives."

"A paradox, indeed, Amos, but you have to realize that there are two kinds of knowledge. Demonstrable knowledge – intellectual knowledge – and instinctive knowledge. The two can be contradictory. They stem from two entirely different spheres from which you can approach the world. On one hand you have the sphere of reason. There, arguments are weighed up against counterarguments and decisions, on which grounds decisions are made.

On the other, you have the emotional sphere. There, feelings dominate, moods, passions, lived experiences. Imagination is rooted in that domain. We use that force to evoke images of things that are impossible to prove in the perceptible, measurable world, but could exist. We imagine because we need them, because those images enrich our lives and give them greater depth.

These two spheres are not exclusive; they are complementary. Imagination provides reason with new ideas, opens new vistas on reality, sometimes even new realities. Likewise, reason protects the imagination from unbridled fantasies. This intuitive knowledge – you could also call it irrational knowledge – says that the soul lives on."

"So is believing in God actually just a question of emotions, of irrational knowledge?"

"Yes it is. In any event my belief in God. I'm emotionally certain, without any intellectual foundation. In that sense, my certainty is entirely subjective. I'm certain, but I can't expect others to share that certainty. There are no objective certainties when it comes to such matters.

You can put it like this, Amos: I'm a believer and therefore I doubt. I'm unsure whether I understand the word of the Lord properly, whether the tribute I pay Him pleases Him, whether He is, indeed, able to conquer death, whether He is responsible for the evil in the world, or whether it's a rival entity, or even man himself, whether a Messiah will appear or whether that's just wishful thinking. My deepest doubt is whether the Lord exists through me or outside of me. Doubt makes me reflect. It's an endless debate."

"This is what it boils down to, Amos: I can offer you no

certainties, only possibilities. You'll have to grapple with your own questions."

"Your words are a relief, Rabbi. You're a relativist. So I can be one, too. I have great difficulty with the absolute truth that many religious officials put forward. I always have questions and the more absolute the way in which they are posed, the more uncertain I become."

Jacob smiled. "I'm glad to have a youthful ally."

"May I just go back to my initial question?"

"Be my guest."

"You still haven't said anything about the idea of the dead being raised again."

"I can deal with that briefly, Amos. I find that idea strange, both intellectually and perceptively. A dead body decays, returns to dust. There's no second round for the body."

"But many Pharisees do embrace that idea, don't they, Jacob? They see that as proof of the Lord's omnipotence. He can even conquer death."

"Even if He were capable, in my view the Lord has no reason whatsoever to do so. Man will have to show what he is worth on earth. The soul, operating independently, can't make up for anything. It can only await reward or punishment. Always assuming, young man, that the soul does, indeed, live on. To tell you the truth, though, Amos, you've worn me out. I'd like to get some sleep now."

"May I just bring up one more point, Rabbi?"

"Go on then."

D. FLUKE?

"When I came in, you asked me, 'What are you doing here?' I've given you an answer. I've asked myself that question, too: 'What am I doing here on Earth? Is it simply a fluke, or is there some purpose behind it and, if so, what is that purpose?' I've got no answer to that question. Can you help me?"

"An age-old question with which many struggle, although the Lord has clearly answered it. He stated, 'Be holy because I, the Lord your God, am holy.'[61] That's the reason. You weren't put on this earth for no particular reason. You have a task."

"To ultimately qualify as holy?"

"That's, indeed, what I believe."

"But I have no idea what is meant by the word 'holy,' Rabbi. Is it about leading an exemplary life? Adhering strictly to the rules? Devoting your life to the study of the Holy Scriptures? Is it about dutifully setting a good example, docilely conforming to what the authorities impose on you? Tell me, please. I understand that the Lord is holy. He represents perfection. For man, though, that's not even imaginable let alone achievable."

"Easy, now, Amos. Listen to the Lord himself. He – as you rightly said, is the ultimate example of holiness – He characterizes Himself as: 'the compassionate and gracious God, slow to anger, abounding in love and faithfulness, maintaining love to thousands, and forgiving wickedness, rebellion and sin . . .' Those qualities are, in principle, also achievable for man. I see that as a command."[62]

"That's quite a tall order, Rabbi. Too tall for many of us, I fear."

"Well, the Lord sets the bar high, my boy. Remember, too, that the qualities He names can be interpreted practically. The Lord created a world that's unfinished, imperfect. You experience that yourself every day. He gave us the opportunity to contribute to creation, to become a kind of assistant creator. So far, we've done very little with that. There's still plenty to do and doing it is what is meant by the term 'holy.' Don't content yourself with the status quo. Try to add value to our society, however modest your contribution may be. Apply it in your life, at home, at work, in the neighborhood where you live."

"So do I have to devote my entire life to the service of others, of society? Isn't that asking too much? There's me, myself, too."

"That's not being asked of you, either, Amos. You don't have to be self-effacing; you have to be indisputably there. Develop yourself, continue developing yourself; that's the motto. If you don't develop yourself, or to put it a better way, evolve, then you won't be able to make much of a contribution to society.

This doesn't go unrewarded, by the way. You enrich and expand your own existence, while gaining significance for others. At best, you fulfil an exemplary function. Your life gains purpose, a goal and therefore meaning."

"That sounds rather grandiose."

"Maybe so, but try reaching high, Amos. Then you'll have something to live for. Make the time you've been given productive. Make sure that, at the end of the journey, you can say: I haven't lived in vain. That's a nice final thought, isn't it?"

Jacob smiled. "I'm not being ironic, my boy, I mean it. Anyway, this is what it boils down to. In His self-characterisation, the Lord gave a blueprint of what He understands to be holy. He leaves the practical interpretation to man."

"You make the concept rather basic, Jacob, almost banal."

"Exactly, the concept is no longer in heaven, any more than our Torah.[63] It's up to man to make the concept worldly."

"You are rather stripping the concept of its heavenly glow, but at least now I know what to do with it."

"Now I really am going to bed, Amos. You can come back tomorrow evening if you like."

E. GOD OR GENIUS?

I went back, eager to continue the conversation. We greeted each other and I immediately started in.

"I'm a doubter and yet, deep in my heart, like you, I have need of certainties. Without my life becoming too complicated."

He answered me in a fatherly fashion. "Keep seeking, young man. You're sure to find subjective certainties. Let that be enough."

"How far does your uncertainty go, Rabbi; all the way?"

"What do you mean?"

"Do you doubt whether the Torah was given by the Lord?"

Jacob gave me a sharp look; almost punitive, I felt. "That, I don't doubt for a moment. If I doubted that I would no longer be a Jew."

"Are you certain the Lord is the author of the Torah?"

He hesitated. "Yes, directly or indirectly."

"What do you mean by indirectly?"

"I mean that Moses was inspired to write it. Inspiration is the ability given to some people to create something entirely new, that didn't exist before. That's inexplicable. It has to be the result of the divine spark, or a salvo of such sparks."

"Does that apply to the numerous interpretations of the law that our sages have formulated over the centuries, as well? Your spiritual peers think so. I understand they consider the Oral Torah to be binding. We have to observe it strictly."

"Yes, that is their view. In addition to the written Torah, the Lord supposedly gave us the Oral Teachings."

"So what's your opinion Rabbi?"

"I consider the Oral Torah to be immensely important. God's rules have to be interpreted and made suitable for application in practice. Time flows and we flow along with it. Society changes. So we need to amend our Teachings. Our sages do that: they've been doing it ever since Moses. Interpretations and reinterpretations have followed one after another, with the sages in constant dialogue with the Lord, as it were. And so the Teachings remain a living organism.

In our circles, there is a saying that the Torah has seventy 'faces,' in other words seventy ways of being read. The number seventy is used to indicate a large number. Explanation and discussion of the Torah is deemed an activity blessed by the Lord. We see these as discussions for, and to the greater glory of, heaven.

The Torah encapsulates an enormous amount of wisdom."

"If I may be so bold though, Rabbi, you haven't answered my

45

question. Does the Oral Torah possess divine imprimatur; was it, like the written Torah, revealed by the Lord? That's what many of your spiritual colleagues claim. Are you of the same opinion?"

For what seemed like several minutes, Jacob said nothing. He sighed deeply and, finally, his answer came.

"Unlike my fellow teachers, I'm not sure about that. Don't forget, though, that I am one of the freethinking Pharisees and even within my branch, my ideas are considered extreme. In my opinion, you can't rule out the possibility of the contents of the Oral Torah having a human imprimatur, coming from our sages themselves. In fact, I think it's quite likely. I can't imagine that, all through the generations, all those sages have been divinely inspired."

Now it was I who sighed deeply.

"You're sighing, Amos, have I shocked you?"

"On the contrary, Jacob, I'm relieved. I'd come to the same conclusion, but I was shocked by my own thoughts. I mean, I thought it was strange that one and the same rule could be assessed so differently, even by people explaining it in the same period. Surely the Lord doesn't give different messages to different sages? Apart from that, new specifications keep being formulated, specifications of specifications. The distance from the fundamental rule is sometimes so great that they're actually new rules. I was wondering whether the Lord had sanctioned all that. I'm relieved because, now that I hear it like this, I see I'm not quite as unworldly as I'd thought."

Jacob lifted his arm and wagged his index finger. "Don't get me wrong, Amos, the Oral Torah is a wise scripture. Wise men don't generally spout nonsense. Study their views, absorb them; just don't accept them blindly. Accept that which you feel brings you closer to the Lord. That's the intention of God's guidelines and, in my view, also that of our exegetes.

I spoke just now of writing, because we've now already spent years setting down the rules that have been passed down orally – our traditions – in writing. But we've still nowhere near finished."

"I admire you, Jacob, you dare to swim against the flow. You've got a lot of hidden strength."

"I'm flattered, my boy, but I'd like to add something to my words. I'm old; most of my life is already behind me. What's more, with everything I've been through in my life I can take a few knocks. Opponents can't floor me that easily. And they do try.

You've got your whole life ahead of you. Keep your doubts to yourself for the time being. Listen, study, reflect, let doubt steer your course, let your conclusions be provisional for now, but don't voice your doubts too loudly. Those who are so certain about it all aren't going to convince you, anyway. Go your own way, but don't make your young life more complicated than necessary. Swimming against the tide is risky. At some point, you may find yourself unable to keep it up and getting swept away."

"I'll try to follow your counsel, but it will be difficult for me not to speak my mind."

Jacob yawned. "I still have so many questions, Rabbi, but aren't I wearing you out?"

"Go on for a while, Amos, but not too long. I like people who ask questions. I'm one myself."

F. TEMPLE OR SYNAGOGUE?

"I go to the Temple quite regularly to make offerings."

"Well, there's nothing wrong with that, my boy. On the contrary: it does you credit."

"Not really, Rabbi; I go there reluctantly."

"You're reluctant to attend services?"

"Yes, it's the sacrificing, the spilling of all that blood. I don't like it. Is that the way to serve the Lord, to honor Him? I don't think He likes it, either. After all, He calls Himself compassionate and gracious, abounding in love and faithfulness.[64] That's not consistent with large-scale slaughter. His love isn't limited to man; it extends to everything that lives. After all, He created all these things.

'The Lord gives life and urges us to choose life.[65] Everything to do with death makes us ritually unclean, unfitting to take part in the Temple service.[66] But the priest lets blood flow freely to serve the Lord. Isn't that inconsistent? What's more, the Lord doesn't need food, as I understand it. He's immaterial, a pure spirit. Spirit feeds on spirit. Remorse, prayer, grace, these are the things that are close to His heart. Isaiah puts it quite succinctly:[67]

> Wash and make yourselves clean,
> take your evil deeds out of my sight,
> stop doing wrong.
> Learn to do right.
> Seek justice,
> defend the oppressed,
> take up the cause of the fatherless,
> plead the case of the widow.

Righteousness will deliver our people,[68] not the needless letting of blood. That's how I see it. And I dare say you do, too."

Jacob nodded in agreement, or so I thought. "I understand you completely, Amos, but what Isaiah describes is the ideal way. We're not ready for that yet. A sacrifice – whatever it might be – means we give something that we own to another, offer it up to show how grateful we are to them. You're right, the Lord should be given spiritual food. Or at least, that's the ideal. We have to grow towards that. Gradually. The Lord knows man inside out. He realizes that a fundamental change of mentality takes time. You can't change people overnight.

Our people have been used to making animal sacrifices since time immemorial. That's the way they served their idols. You can't simply do away with that pattern. It takes time. Time and alternatives. We've understood that, we Pharisees and our predecessors. We've started developing ways to reach the Lord,

48

ways that don't reject, but complement the Temple, that make the service more personal and more spiritual.

As you know, we organize gatherings for local residents. There, we learn together; we pray and sing together. That way, we get to know each other better. It brings the community together and lifts it out of the everyday. You'll be familiar with these 'synagogues' from your own experience. I hope and expect that sacrificing will die a death, and that it will be replaced by the gatherings in synagogues and the Temple will become the central synagogue."

"So that's how you relativize the significance of the Temple?"

"Well, I'd like to put it another way. I think the synagogue is important and the current Temple services are not satisfactory. I agree with you that they're too impersonal and too aloof. What's more, I don't have much time for our current Temple servants. The high priest is appointed by the Roman authorities and dances to their tune. He no longer has much authority amongst the people. A lot of priests are corrupt and demand fat fees for their services. The synagogue is already popular now and so are we, the Pharisees. We've become the new spiritual elite.[69] The priests have started colluding with the rich and powerful in our society, with the establishment, and you could typify the Sadducees in that respect. They've distanced themselves too far from the people."

"So, in the future you're painting, will priests become superfluous?"

"Not necessarily. We could start working with them. We, the Pharisees, offer them the components for a new religious service. They build that up into a standardized ritual and stand behind it. In that model, we Pharisees would remain the teachers."

"You amaze me, Rabbi. You seem to be speaking like a politician, rather than a religious teacher."

"Make no mistake, my boy. Many a time Pharisees have walked and have to walk the path of politics. Without our support, it would often have been difficult for our rulers to implement administrative measures. Yes, in supporting them we've regularly intervened in state affairs. We've been promoted to the voice of the people."

"I know, and the people are very grateful to you for that. But I'd just like to come back for a moment to the vision of the future that you just outlined. Phariseeship isn't hereditary, but priesthood is. Should things stay that way?"

"Not for priesthood. I don't understand why the Lord declared it to be hereditary at the time. The criteria for being granted a function in a house dedicated to the Lord shouldn't be origin but suitability, measured against such aspects as knowledge, wisdom and a focus on your fellow man: such characteristics aren't automatically transferred from generation to generation. Phariseeship is not handed to you on a silver platter, either. You have to study hard for it."

"The priests won't be too pleased to receive that message, Jacob. You're undermining established interests, promoting revolutionary politics!"

"No I'm not. I'm just thinking ahead."

"But your ideas are confrontational; they could cause a division in society."

"You're right. Which is why, so far, I haven't been spouting them in public. We Pharisees have to try and keep the relationship with the priests workable and not throw fat into a smouldering fire. That means – and here I come back to your question – that, for the moment, sacrificing has to be honored." His voice sounded pertinent. "Otherwise, we would not only elicit major conflicts with the priests; we would also throw the people into confusion. For the moment, the synagogue complements the Temple; it's not an alternative."

"I've just got one more question, Jacob, the last for the time being. May I?"

"You may, Amos. You're time-consuming and exhausting, but fascinating. I therefore stress 'for the time being.'"

F. FREE MAN OR PUPPET?

"I'm still struggling with another question, Jacob. Does man possess free will? I'm hearing contradictory noises. I heard a priest claim that it's fully free.[70] There's no way it can be otherwise. He said The Lord is without sin and unable to discern sins. It's up to men to distinguish between good and evil. Once created, man is left to his own devices. I don't understand how he came to that conclusion. If I read Moses' scriptures, then the image arises of a father figure, concerned for his children.

The ultra-religious who live in our neighborhood – Essenes they call themselves – believe exactly the opposite. In their view, man has no free will. The Lord has already mapped out the course of our lives in advance.[71] I find that concept even stranger, disquieting in a certain sense. I want to construct my own life and I feel that's what I'm doing, that I'm responsible for it myself and that I can't shift that responsibility onto others. I, myself, am at the helm of my ship. It's I who determine the course, not the ship. That's the way I see it."

Jacob smiled, "I thought you'd say something like that, but now it's my turn to ask question: where do you get your wisdom?"

"I get it from the Torah; not the least of sources, eh, Rabbi?" I answered, confidently. "The Lord created free people who can decide for themselves how to organize their lives. You can read that in the Book of Deuteronomy.[72] They've regularly abused that freedom, since the very beginning. Adam and Eve defied God's will. Their sons didn't do much better. Cain beat Abel to death out of pure jealousy. Transgression was the order of the day. The Lord was so disappointed in his ultimate creation that he was at the point of eradicating mankind. Ultimately, he didn't do so.[73] Why not? I think because he believed in free will, in the capacity of man to improve his life.

Abraham, the founding father of our people, was given the task of forming a vanguard for a society the Lord was envisioning, based on righteousness, justice and respect for others. That goal can only be achieved by free men who are able to say yes or no.

And finally, Rabbi, the Lord ended our enslavement in Egypt. Why? Because a man shouldn't be a slave, subject to the whims of his master. He must be able to take his destiny into his own hands. That's the only way he can give his life meaning, make something of it, or fritter it away.

For me, it's clear: we've been created with a free will. After all, why should the Lord have wanted to create puppets, walking on His leash? That would have done Him no credit."

Jacob looked satisfied, it seemed to me. "You're a budding teacher, my boy. Now allow me to raise an objection," he said, smiling. "If man does, indeed, decide his own fate, then what remains of God's omnipotence? Does He relinquish it?"

"No, Rabbi, you don't always have to exercise power, or, to put it a better way: you can use power to limit your power."

"A nice thought, Amos, but it's seldom put into practice. Let me say this, though: you used to come to me to learn. Now, I'm learning from you. It's the best thing that can happen to a teacher.

Let me summarize what I think about free will. I like to have it both ways. The Lord is aware of everything that will happen to us. After all, he decides that himself. Thanks to His omnipotence, though, He is prepared and able to give people the freedom of choice.[74] In due time, people will have to account for their choices."

"In due time? Do you mean in the coming world?"

"Yes, I do."

"But I thought you doubted its existence."

"And so I do, but this is where imagination helps me out. I already told you as much. I imagine that a coming world exists and that the soul won't die. My intellect is incapable of erasing those images. I can live quite comfortably with that contradiction. In fact, if intellect alone were to be sanctifying, then my life would lose a great deal of its color and scent."

I stood up from my chair. "May I offer you an alternative, though? Perhaps the 'final judgement' is fiction, nothing more than our own conscience. It applauds decent behavior and makes us feel guilty when we do wrong. Feeling guilty is an inescapable punishment."

"Feeling guilty is, indeed, a punishment, but some people's conscience is poorly developed. They have hardly any feelings of guilt.

In short, my boy, this won't do. There are questions to which we find no answers. It doesn't matter, though. We'll continue to search. It keeps us on our toes.

But now I really have to go. I've already spent a lot of time with you, but it was certainly worthwhile."

G. LAST MINUTE

"Please, Rabbi, just one last-minute question."

"Your perseverance is impressive, Amos. Go on, then."

"You have some criticism of the Temple service, as I understand it."

Jacob nodded; acquiescently, I thought. "On the other hand, the Lord gave instructions to build the *Mishkan* (Hebrew: the Tabernacle) so that He could dwell among us, the Israelites.[75] Surely, the *Mishkan* was the mobile predecessor of our Temple? The place is holy and irreplaceable, isn't it?"

"No, my boy. In a nutshell: the Lord doesn't live in a tabernacle, or in a Temple. The Lord has no spatial limits. He is infinite. He lives in the mind of those whose hearts attempt to approach Him. 'Among those (. . .) I will be proved holy.'[76] That closeness is found not only in the Temple but also in the synagogue. The Temple as a spatial structure is important, but not indispensable.

Just one more thing, Amos, before I go. You're a doubter at heart. Stay that way, but beware of excessive doubt. Believing in the existence of the Lord is, in essence, a dream, a noble dream. The loveliest dream anyone can have. Remember that dreams can contain a great deal of truth. Don't destroy that dream with doubt. That will do nothing to enrich your life."

He crossed to the door. "Farewell, Amos. And don't be a stranger."

"Thank you for your patience, thank you for trusting me, thank you for what you have taught me."

He waved and went through the door.

I stayed sitting for a moment. An inspiring person, I thought, but certainly no rock of security. He nuances his remarks. That means he relativizes. Beware of false securities, he seems to be saying to me. They encourage complacency and generate intolerance towards those who think differently. That is so, but if you over-refine a vision, little more remains of it than a shadow. I was still uncertain.

CHAPTER 3

JUDA, A PRIEST

Creating a paradise on earth was not something the Lord saw as one of His tasks. That was a task He had intended for man.

As an animal dies, so a man dies, too; all have the same breath . . . All go to the same place; all come from dust, and to dust all return. Who knows if the human spirit rises upward and if the spirit of the animal goes down into the earth?

Ecclesiastes 3:19, 20–12

A. THE RUN-UP

I went back home and told my father how I had got on. "Jacob turned out to be a Pharisee from the ultra-freethinking camp, Father. A wonderful man, a thinker, but he couldn't offer me any certainty; on the contrary, he actually made me even more uncertain. What do you think I should do?"

Father put his arm around me. "Don't stop there, boy. Continue your quest. Pharisees are learned, but there are so many more ideas under the Jewish sun. There is a priest living not far from here, one from a high-priestly family. His name is Juda. I know him vaguely; I recently made two silver candlesticks for one of his sons. Go to him and say that you're my son."

"Do you think he could introduce me to the High Priest?"

"What?" said my father, surprised, "The High Priest? What are you thinking of?"

55

"Well, he's at the top of the priestly pyramid, isn't he? Surely he's the most learned amongst them?"

"Whatever gave you that idea? That's never been the case. It's ancestry that determines the appointment of a High Priest, not knowledge.[16] And that's not even the case nowadays. The Roman procurator appoints and dismisses him as he sees fit. His criterion isn't knowledge, but submissiveness, the degree to which a candidate is willing to dance to his tune. Yes, the High Priest does still enjoy some authority, political authority, because he presides over our high court, the Sanhedrin, and he's responsible for peace and order in our land. But only in that sense is he the first among equals.

You don't need to speak to the High Priest and you won't get to speak to him anyway. So you can forget that idea."

I set off and found Juda's house in the upper part of Jerusalem. It was an impressive property, almost a small palace. I knocked. After a while, the door was opened by a short, slightly bent man with a sharp face, a big nose and bright, red-rimmed eyes. It was hard to say how old he was, but he was evidently much older than me. Despite his modest physique, he made a highly-venerable impression.

"Are you Juda, the priest?"

"Yes, I am. Who are you?"

"I'm Amos, Mordechai the silversmith's son."

"Oh, yes, I remember him. What do you want here?" he continued, coolly.

I felt he was being condescending. That awakened the provocateur in me. I ignored my father's advice and, summoning my courage, said,

"I'd like to speak to the High Priest. Could you introduce me to him?" I was curious to hear Juda's answer.

His mouth dropped open in astonishment. After a couple of seconds, he replied crossly, "The High Priest? Who do you think you are? Do you think the man has time for a boy like you, an ordinary youth? Are you not aware of his role? It's the High

Fig. 4 The 2nd Temple in Jerusalem, which was enlarged and embellished
by King Herod and destroyed by the Romans in 70 CE.
From: Rosenberg, S. and Mevorah, (Eds) (2013). *Herod the Great. The
King's final Journey.* Jerusalem: The Israel Museum.

For centuries, the Temple in Jerusalem was the center of worship services
for the Lord. These were led by priests. In the early years of the first century, the house of learning/place of worship, led by legal scholars, already
occupied an important place. This institution was the precursor of the synagogue. Did it complement or rival the Temple service? Opinions varied.

Priest who connects us with and binds us to the Almighty. He's got other things to think about. Go on home. You should be ashamed of yourself."

I wasn't going to be put off so lightly. "But surely, Master, it's not just the elite that the High Priest connects to the Almighty. I can't imagine he leaves the common man out in the cold. If so, then may the Lord forgive him."

Juda said nothing, doubtless trying to think of a fitting response. Then came, "You're extraordinarily insolent, which doesn't endear you to me, but I won't send you away because your reply is valid. The High Priest is there for all of us. That's how it should be. You seem a sincere young man."

Juda let me in, waving me to a chair.

"Does that mean I can talk to you about my problems?"

"So, you'll content yourself with second choice, will you?" he laughed mockingly.

"No, Master, that's not what I meant." I was quiet for a moment. Now, it was I who was searching for words. I found them. "You're not second choice; you're a different choice. The High Priest represents authority, while you and your colleagues represent knowledge. The two don't necessarily go together. On reflection, I think I may even be better off with you."

He smiled. "Well, that's a nice way of putting it. I don't know if you mean what you say, but stay and tell me what's troubling you."

I stood up again and began pacing back and forth. "These aren't questions you hear every day, Juda."

He stopped me. "Don't beat around the bush, boy; get the point and, by the way, my name is not Juda, it's Judas."

"Judas? You've Hellenized your name?"

"Not me; it was my father."

"But you kept it."

"Evidently. Do you have an objection? If so, then your sincerity is bordering on insolence."

I took the hint. Watch out, I thought, or you'll annoy him and he'll send you away.

"No, I've got no objection, Judas. It was merely an observation. I can understand it. The Roman oppressors see you priests as our leaders, I imagine. And you have to see that the communication channels are kept open. Obviously, that requires some accommodation."

"I suspect you're twisting your words again and you do have an objection. Well, you're not the only one. It's seen as cowardice. But it's not. We do, indeed, attempt to keep relations with the Romans workable and prevent worse. That demands concessions on our part. I'll make you a concession. You can call me Juda. To be honest I, myself, prefer to hear that name. I'm a great admirer of our namesake."

"I appreciate that, Juda. Now, about me. In a nutshell, I'm in a bind. I *am* a Jew, from a formal point of view. I want to *be* a Jew and I have doubts."

"About what?" Juda asked, interested.

"About how a Jew should be on the 'inside.' I mean, the way he structures his spiritual existence. What is it that shows him the way in life? I hear so many conflicting views. I've lost the way: I no longer know who I should believe, what I should believe and, if I don't believe in that, whether that means I'm no longer a Jew."

Juda threw up his arms, as if in despair. The gesture appeared both affected and stagy. "My son, my son," he said, "Have you thoroughly studied the instructions of our great teacher Moses?"

"Quite thoroughly, Juda, and that's why I've got questions."

"Haven't you discussed them with your father?"

"Yes, of course, but he didn't have any answers, so he recommended I seek scholarly advice."

"Well, I'll do my best. This is the first time I've been asked such a question." Juda pushed back his chair and settled down to answer.

B. DOES HE EXIST THROUGH ME OR I THROUGH HIM?

"Your question isn't complicated, young man. I can't understand why you haven't got an answer. How you should think and live as a Jew? According to God's instructions, and those you can read in Moses' scriptures."

"As I said, that's where my problems begin. First my key question. I suspect this will make you cross, but I'm going to risk it anyway. You talk about God's instructions. Are they actually God's instructions and, even more fundamentally, does the Lord actually exist?"

This time, Juda's anger was no longer feigned; he banged his fist on the table and barked, "What kind of a question is that, boy? The question alone profanes God's name."

"No, it doesn't, Juda, or at least that's not my intention. My question actually honors the Lord."

"Oh, really? Well, I'm curious to see how you talk yourself out of that!"

"The Lord came to us as a transcendent, abstract being; extra-sensorial, imageless, timeless, limitless, with no name pronounceable by man. That image appeals to me. In our Holy Scriptures, though, he took on an increasingly concrete, humanized form. He revealed himself as a strict, but benign father figure. That was just a guise, though. Supposedly enabling us to imagine and accept Him more easily.

I'm not comfortable with that idea. In my perception, the Creator is actually the counterpart of the worldly and the material. He's pure spirit, an inexhaustible, constantly-renewing source of wisdom and creative power. A being, yes, but one that's otherwise undefinable. We experience, rather than know Him. If I imagine anything, then it's the image of a Super-Moses, a superior teacher and mentor. He's either that or an illusion.

If he's the former, then I don't understand how we can be created in God's image. We consist overwhelmingly of matter and most of us aren't endowed with much wisdom or creative power.

If He's the latter, then that would undermine the foundation of our Holy Scriptures."

I could see my words were increasingly irritating Juda, but he restrained himself.

"Listen and learn, young man. You're barking up the wrong tree. I'll answer your questions, but let that be an end to the matter. No further discussion!

You exist, don't you, Amos? You exist because your parents existed. They existed because Adam once existed. So where did he come from? Did he appear out of thin air? Well, in a certain sense, yes. He was created. By whom? By the Lord. The fact that you're sitting there is the best proof that the Lord is no illusion."

Now it was I who was starting to get irritated. "You can't fob me off like that, Juda. This is a fundamental question. How do you obtain certainty of the actual existence of an abstraction? The world and everything living was created. Okay. That's a fact. The how and why are a puzzle to me, though, a mystery. Perhaps that's what the answer should be."

"No, that's not the answer – you're enticing me into a debate, after all – I'll give you another argument. Moses, our great teacher, spoke directly to the Lord and He gave Moses His insight.[17] Those Teachings are the soil in which our people is rooted. There's no doubt about that."

I interrupted him. "But that's precisely what I do have doubts about or, rather, questions. After Moses, when prophets spoke with the Lord it was never directly, only in dreams and visions.[18] Even Moses didn't get to see God's face.[19] Of course, abstractions don't have faces. That's their strength. It's why they have more authority, why they exercise more influence than anything or anyone in the concrete reality, but, at the same time, they evoke uncertainty. That's their weakness. How 'real' is the abstraction? In the case of Moses: did the voice Moses heard come from outside him or from within? Could Moses have formulated our Teachings on his own?"

"On his own, Amos? Can a man formulate a message that

will constitute the principal for a totally new social order all by himself?"

"It is possible, Juda, with genius. There are people – artists, writers, architects, poets, philosophers – whose creative ability can bring about revolutions. Geniuses are potential innovators."

"Okay, but then what is that 'genius,' Amos, you tell me."

I was quiet for a moment. "I don't know. That puzzles me, it's a mystery . . . Perhaps there's a divine spark."

"Now you're on the right road. Genius: the result of a divine spark, our Teachings being the result of a divine fire. Hold that thought, young man. Assimilate Moses' scriptures and live according to them, then you will prosper."

"But Juda, that 'divine spark' is a metaphor, a 'manner of speaking.' I just can't imagine it being an almighty Creator."

"You don't have to imagine anything. You said yourself that the word 'God' conjures up no images for you. Believing, that's what it's all about. Knowing through believing. Knowing internally without having any proof."

I didn't respond to his words, but continued, "There's something else I can't imagine either, Juda."

"And what might that be, son?"

"That everything came into the world ready-made. Was there then no evolution at all?"

"That's what we have been told, what's been passed down and, ultimately, written down."

"But surely, Juda, everything that lives develops. A child grows in its mother's belly, a plant from a seed, a tree from a sapling."

Juda laughed, somewhat scornfully. "Do you imagine that doubt somehow marks you as a courageous person?"

"No, Juda, I don't think that; I'm not courageous; it's more like vacillating. I shift awkwardly from one standpoint to another and back again. That doesn't make my life any simpler, but it does make it more interesting. I think, or rather, I believe the Lord allows me that; perhaps even expects it of me. He provided man with possibilities, not certainties. I wonder whether I'll ever reach the finish line.

You're a pious man, but do you never have any doubts?"

"Smart alec," smiled Juda, as he left the room.

C.   BELIEF, ACCEPTANCE OR SUBMISSION?

After a while, he came back with a big pot of tea, poured me a cup and sat down again.

"Do I ever have my doubts? Now and again, but not often; praise the Lord."

"Do you faithfully obey all the commandments?"

"As far as possible."

"All of them? Even those you don't see the point of?"

"Yes, I do. This feels like a cross examination, Amos."

"It's not a cross examination, Juda, I'm just trying to understand what you see as important in life, what you consider to be the essence. I don't understand why you would practice laws whose meaning you don't comprehend."

"I don't see what there is not to understand. I obey them because they were imposed by the Lord. Evidently, He had His reasons. Who am I to be as wise, or even wiser, than the Lord?"

"I have difficulty accepting that view, Juda. The Lord blessed me with the ability to judge and He expects me to use that ability. If I obey a law without conviction, then I feel hypocritical. I assume the Lord sets more store by sincerity than by superficial appearances. I admit that my frame of thinking certainly isn't unlimited in scope, but that frame is what He allotted me and I have to make do with it. I can't think outside of it.

I do sometimes think the Lord Himself must have doubts. Did I do the right thing? Might I have gone too far, too far beyond the reasonable? Should I perhaps review the laws I set down then, adapt them to changing circumstances? Perhaps I should call in the wise men to do this. They know the circumstances, they live with them. They're best placed to judge whether anything should be done and, if so, what.

He must have his doubts, Juda. We're created in His image. So nothing human can be alien to Him."

Juda looked at me with some astonishment. "I'm listening to you with fascination, young man, but also concern. You go too far. You talk about the Lord as if He were one of your close friends."

"Well, that's how I experience Him, Juda. I don't talk *about* the Lord, I talk *with* Him. I think and I doubt – I might almost say 'therefore' I doubt. I ask Him questions and listen to, or should I say experience, the reply. Often, I don't take it on face value and enter into a debate."

"That's all very well, Amos, as long as your attitude is that of a pupil speaking to his mentor. When I hear you speak like this, though, it seems as if you see your role as that of a colleague with a different point of view, who sometimes might know better. That's going too far. You can ask questions, but you mustn't question the Teachings, deciding for yourself which rules you'll abide by and which you won't. Otherwise, you're eroding the foundation on which our society stands, destabilizing it and making it easy prey for the idolaters who surround us."

"I'm not so sure of that. If more and more people start sharing my doubts, but fail to express them, if the tone is set by hypocrisy, then that will generate internal rot. Now, that would be really dangerous. Our Teachings rely on belief, not subjugation."

"I'm not talking about subjugation, son, I'm talking about acceptance. Acceptance is the result of learning and learning again, your whole life through; internalizing the matter and, ultimately, conforming to it."

"That assumes respect for the teacher, for his knowledge and insight."

"Yes, Amos, it does."

"But sometimes students are wiser, or become wiser, than the teacher."

"That certainly doesn't apply to our great teacher Moses or the super Teacher, the Lord."

"Of course not, but if I don't understand something I ask questions. I'm seeking certainty, Juda. I thought our belief would provide it."

"Then you got it wrong, son. You talk about belief. You don't have to believe very much; no more than that our Lord is the one God and that He gave Moses binding instructions on Mount Sinai. The Lord doesn't demand belief; He demands acts; here on Earth. We can decide to follow either a righteous path in our lives or a path that will turn out to be a dead end or one of the many ways in between. That's our choice. The Jewish philosophy of life offers us possibilities, not certainties. And now I'm repeating your own words. Surely, you haven't forgotten them?"

Juda began impatiently drumming his fingers on the table top. "I have to say, you seem to be an incorrigible smart alec. I suspect you see yourself in the super-wise student you spoke of. Enough of this, though. I won't let you have the last word."

"I'll swallow my last word, then, but I've still got some questions. May I?"

"Well, go on then."

"I'll be concrete. What, for example, is the sense of our dietary laws? I mean the deeper, spiritual sense. They make it difficult to mix with our gentile compatriots. That really annoys me."

"Maybe so, but that's exactly the point of them. Keep away from their way of living, their views, and their practices. We've been ordered to be different from them; to become quartermasters of a society that, in many respects, is the opposite of theirs."

"So it's chiefly about preventing spiritual contamination, then, is it?"

"That's right, Amos."[20]

"But I'm not worried about that at all, Juda. My belief is as solid as a rock. I've got questions, yes, but I am a Jew, through and through. The Torah is the hub around which my life revolves.

The Lord is my mentor and always will be. Nonetheless, I'm curious as to what our neighbors have to say. Certainly, there is much that I reject. The pantheon of rival gods that they worship is more likely to make me laugh than admire them; I find naked men competing in sports distasteful. On the other hand, I often find their philosophical views elucidating, their poetry impressive, not as a replacement for but as a complement to the Torah.

We have to set ourselves apart, you say. Well, then, let's do that through our behavior, by attempting to be a 'light to the nations.' After all, that light isn't spread through our eating habits."

"It is partly, Amos. It illustrates the importance we attach to controlling urges." Almost snarling, he added, "The pleasures of the Hellenistic world you speak of are a slippery slope. Before you know it, you can slide into the abyss. Your questions show that you're already well on your way.

But leaving this intellectual brawling aside: the dietary laws were imposed on us by the Lord. If you reject them, then what you're actually doing is rejecting His authority."

Juda was obviously keen to bring the discussion to an end, so I didn't push the matter.

"Our opinions are incompatible, Juda. The only conclusion I can draw is that both are correct, both are incorrect, or one of them should be rejected. I'll have to make do with that.

Could I ask you one more similar question about meaning, though?" Without awaiting his reply, I went on, "This one is about the purity and cleanliness laws. We have to do our best to remain morally clean. That's fine, but I'm confused about ritual cleanliness. Like the priests, I have to be clean when I enter the Temple.[21] Like you, I must not have been in contact with the dead or anything to do with the dead. But what does the Lord have against the dead? I don't understand that."

"You don't understand, or you don't want to understand? The Lord represents the everlasting, the eternal. He created life.

Man was His ultimate creation and Death equals decomposition, the opposite of life. He finds it distasteful."

"But Juda, it was He Himself who irrevocably linked life to death."

"No, Amos, man himself is responsible for that. You know what happened in the Garden of Eden."[22]

"So you hold Eve and Adam's behavior responsible for our mortality?"

"Yes. Evidently, the Lord would have liked things to turn out differently. I think that explains His aversion to everything reminiscent of man's mortality."

"Well, I can't reconcile myself with that explanation. Surely we're judged by our own deeds and not held responsible for the mistakes of our distant ancestors.[23] That aside, though, Juda, I interpret Adam and Eve's trials and tribulations differently. In my view, the Lord was testing them."

"Yes, He was. The Lord was testing their obedience. What is 'different' about your view?"[24]

"I believe it wasn't their obedience the Lord was testing but their independence."

"What do you mean?"

"It surely couldn't have been God's intention to populate the world with what amounts to puppets – entirely dependent on God's guidance morally, weaned from any lust for knowledge, incapable of or at least unwilling to work towards a decent, dignified society; a carefree parasite in and on a Kingdom of God, living in a habitat that was already perfect and in which any initiative would, therefore, have been superfluous and concepts such as challenge and progress were unknown, in which evil didn't exist and belief would have degenerated into a rudimentary, if not redundant, spiritual attribute. I repeat, that couldn't have been God's intention.

The Lord didn't create saints; He created people with good and bad traits, deliberately I assume. A being that was given the possibility to accentuate his good side, or his dark side.

From a human perspective, it seems likely to me that for-
bidding them to eat the fruit of the tree of knowledge of good
and bad was actually a test. 'Have I, God, created a being with
enough initiative, with enough altruistic awareness, with enough
thirst for knowledge to build a society that has a chance of ful-
filling My criteria? If so, then they will ignore My command.'

And that's what happened. God had, indeed, created a *person*.
Eve, the main 'culprit,' became the matriarch of the ideal person:
equally moral and intellectually gifted. God 'punishes' the first
couple by banishing them from 'Paradise.' In fact, the way I
interpret that text, he gives them the possibility to set out on the
path towards a society that will ultimately please Him. They're
given the chance to lead a life worth living.[25]

The so-called fall of man, the way I see it, was actually a 'blessing in disguise.' Thanks to the first people's decision, man was
blessed with not only a thirst for knowledge and morality, but
also the ability to believe. Adam and Eve themselves may lose
paradise, but they gain belief. The Lord speaks to them after the
'offense' and they answer him. That engenders communication.
Surely, communication between Him and man is the real char-
acteristic of religious belief."

"What a tirade, young man! Such fine words! But it's nothing
other than wild speculation."

"Daring, possibly, Juda, but not wild."

"Too wild. The Lord didn't create paradise just to promptly
kick the first people out of it. That land wasn't only intended
for the animals. Knowledge of good and evil was counter-pro-
ductive. Gaining knowledge of evil leads to evil. The command
the Lord gave the first people was basic. Breaking it was a sin,
literally a mortal sin. And so mortality made its entrance."

"I still see it differently, Juda. Creating a paradise on Earth
wasn't something the Lord saw as one of His tasks. That was a
task He had intended for man."

"Don't be such a know-it-all, boy. Don't act as if you're

68

rivalling God's wisdom. He won't stand for that. You know what happened to Lucifer."[26]

I continued, unabated.

"The thing I don't understand, Juda, is that the Lord whom, you say, wants to stay away from death, from transience, lets Himself be honored with the large-scale killing of animals, which are, after all, His creations. Surely that's inconsistent."

"Again, it doesn't have to be consistent, Amos. That's just what the Lord does. You accept it."

I thought for a moment.

"I can't, Juda. For me, acceptance is preceded by understanding. May I go on for just a moment, or am I annoying you too much?"

"Actually, you are, but, like everyone, you have the right to speak."

"So, why does a man become ceremonially unclean by spontaneous ejaculation and a woman by menstruation?[27,28] After all, we have no control over those processes. They are, I thought, 'embedded.' By whom? By the Lord Himself."

Juda tapped his fingers impatiently on the table again.

"Has your father taught you nothing, boy? Go on, though."

"He did his best, but he was often lost for words. That's why he sent me to you."

Juda gave me a suspicious look. "You must be kidding, Amos!"

"No, I'm telling the truth."

"Okay, I'll believe you then. In the cases you quote, there is the issue of a potential waste of life. The lining of the uterus could have nourished a new embryo. The spent seed could have fertilized a woman's egg. The Lord is a God of life and the living.[29] He's averse to wasting potential life."[30]

I nodded. "And after the cleansing ritual, the Lord welcomes you back?"

"Yes, He does."

"That matter is clear to me now, Juda."

"I'm glad you at least understand something, Amos, but go home now. You look exhausted."

"I'm excited and that's tiring. May I come back again?"

"Yes, you may," he laughed, closing the door behind me.

D.   TEMPLE OR SYNAGOGUE?

Watch your words, Amos, I thought when I returned the following evening. Your questions are obviously disturbing Juda.

"I've got another question that's probably sensitive," I began, "But I'm going to ask it anyway. You've got an open mind."

"I don't need buttering up, Amos, speak up."

"I'm really bothered about the ritual of offerings, especially where animals are concerned. Their panicky fear, the flowing blood, the cutting open of their bodies: I can't see anything spiritual, anything divine there. I have an aversion to it. Can you understand that?"

Juda looked stern. "That understanding of yours again. What do you want to understand? You don't have to understand anything. Just do what's set down clearly and unambiguously in Leviticus. That's God's will."

"I know that, Juda, but I can't understand how it can be His will. 'Blood is the force of life' He says;[31] 'Choose life,' don't choose death.[32] Death makes us ceremonially unclean.[33] Death isn't elevated, as I understand it, it's the diametric opposite of the sacred. So surely that also applies to the killing, itself."

Juda thought for a moment and then answered, hesitantly, "You are right in a certain sense," and here he faltered, "The offering means you're prepared to sacrifice something for the Lord. That's how you should see the offering."

The standard answer. Obviously, I wasn't convinced. "To me, that ritual is far too much like a bribe, an attempt at appeasement, at buying Him off. I get a priest to make an offering, in the hopes that the Lord will turn a blind eye to my wrongdoing. And, what's more, the animal only has a monetary value. You're offering something from your possessions. That's the kind of gift you give your fellow man, surely, not the Lord. He expects something with a spiritual content, something that comes from within you, not from your pocket. Relinquish some vanity, for example, some self-importance, haughtiness, or miserliness; donate what benefits society: knowledge, attention, time. That's the kind of offering that's at the Lord's level.

In any case, what in God's name is He supposed to do with sacrificial animals? He has no material existence; He consists of pure spirit. What He needs is spiritual food."

Juda was becoming visibly impatient. "That may be what you think, young man," he retorted. "But the Lord has never mentioned it. Follow what's written. Do you think you're above the Law? What are you trying to say? You're putting yourself and others on the wrong track with your talk!"

"Excuse me, Juda, but the Lord *has* mentioned it. When He led our forefathers out of Egypt, He never said or prescribed anything to do with burnt or peace offerings. What I commanded you to do, He said, is to 'be obedient.'[34] Please don't get upset, though, Juda," I said, "These are just questions; they're not criticism."

"Be honest, Amos, you are criticizing. Your questions show you don't take the subject seriously."

My self-confidence was restored. "Oh, but I do take the subject seriously. Extremely seriously even, which is why I'm asking questions. We were created in God's image and therefore as free people. Free, mature people ask questions; they don't allow themselves to be muzzled and they do allow themselves to be corrected when the criticism is justified."

"You're a skilled debater, Amos, I'll give you that, but remember that the Lord doesn't allow himself to be overruled. Anyone who thinks he can do that will have a rude awakening. Make no mistake about that."

Now it was I who began to feel irritated. "I'll ignore that threat, Master," I said curtly. "The Lord freed slaves; he didn't make them. Our forefathers weren't afraid to speak their mind; they offered criticism: Abraham, Moses, Job and many others. And they got away with it. The Lord listened. In fact, He sometimes changed course. He didn't silence anyone and *you* can't silence *me*. After all, the Lord is a role model for you, priest. But let's not allow things to get heated. I respect your opinion. Please show some understanding for mine."

Juda stared rigidly across the room. "I'll say it again: you're too bold, bordering on the insolent" – his tone was measured – "But I will attempt to show some understanding."

"I suspect you'll find my next point even more inappropriate, but I'm going to put it to you, nonetheless. The Temple isn't enough for me, personally. To put it bluntly, I can't get things off my chest there."

"What do you mean, Amos?"

"Well, there are often things I've done, or haven't done, that I regret. You priests prescribe a simple remedy for that. Show remorse and have an offering made in the Temple, by a priest, naturally. As far as I'm concerned, that's a stopgap. It doesn't help enough or long enough."

Juda's face hardened. "It's the royal route to reconciliation with the Lord, boy!"

"That may be so but, first and foremost, I'm seeking reconciliation with myself, reconciliation with the person who is so different from the one I would have liked to be. You have the same recipe for everyone, but we're not all the same."

"We are when it comes to guilt feelings. That's a feeling that hardly differs from individual to individual. A universal approach is quite appropriate there. Take the Day of Atonement. That's the one day you have the chance to unburden your soul. Not all alone, but all together. Together with everyone else who has anything to confess. Then you feel you aren't the only one with something to admit to; there are lots of you. That alone is a relief."

"I can't crop everything up until then, Juda. Apart from which, there's a risk I might forget things."

"Well, the sin can't be as bad as all that, then, Amos," laughed Juda. I didn't respond.

"That day doesn't provide me with enough solace, either. It's a ritualized display in my view. Everything proceeds according to a neatly-prescribed pattern. Year after year. The High Priest first confesses his own sins, then those of his 'house' and then those of our people. Yes, I'm a member of that people but, for me, this lacks a personal approach. My neighbor might have something to confess, too, but you can't tar all sins and all sinners with one brush. I want to speak personally, be addressed personally. Not as part of one big whole. I've misbehaved as an individual and I'd like to rehabilitate myself as an individual, without anyone's intervention, spontaneously, and not through all kinds of en-trenched rituals."

"You underestimate the importance of the group event and of ritual, Amos. Left to their own devices, many people aren't sure what to do with guilt feelings. They seek a ritual, a structured way of confessing and ridding themselves of those feelings. They have a need for peers, for people in a similar boat to themselves. Once they've jointly complied with that prescribed pattern, they feel better, relieved."

"Well, that may be so for the majority, but not for me. The High Priest addresses the Lord. I address myself; I want to come to terms with myself. That conversation isn't always easy. Then I need help, private help. My neighbor will have to fend for himself. To be honest, Juda, where this is concerned, I seek my salvation away from the Temple."

"I suppose you're alluding to the synagogue."

"Yes, I am. I talk to my teacher there. I pray there, I enter into dialogue with myself and that's how I manage to move on; that's how I unburden my conscience."

"I'm not saying I don't understand you, Amos, but I can't make the Temple service anything other than what it is. I wouldn't

73

want to, either. The Lord wrote that script. And don't forget what a disaster it would be if we no longer had the Temple. The sun around which the Jewish planet revolves would go out, with a serious risk of that planet veering away from its orbit. The Temple symbolizes the unity and uniqueness of the Lord and of our people. You have to realize that."

"You're too pessimistic, Juda. Even in such a terrible scenario, our people wouldn't be irretrievably lost. In that case, the synagogue would keep our people together. *That* would become the Temple of our Torah. The Torah isn't bound to the Temple in Jerusalem; it goes with us wherever we go."

"I'm afraid our people wouldn't survive such a disaster."

"We will survive, Juda, until we've fulfilled the mission the Lord has given us and I suspect that mission will never be completed."

A servant came in with a bowl of fruit and a carafe of juice. At just the right moment, it occurred to me.

"I generally have a little something around this time, Amos. Let's take a break. Will you join me?"

Some twenty minutes later, Juda indicated that we should resume our discussion. "So what else bothers you about our Temple, then?"

"As if that wasn't enough! But I'd like to ask you something very personal, Juda. How do you feel when you carry out the sacrificial ritual? Uncomfortable, like me? Do you ever think, 'should I be doing this? Will this really find favour with the Lord? Would this really make the one on whose orders I'm acting feel good?'"

"No, my boy, on the contrary. I'm doing God's will. I consider that a privilege. The same goes for the penitent, I'm sure."

I could feel myself getting annoyed again. I thought, 'Juda, in my opinion you're misunderstanding God's being. He must be horrified by those bloodbaths. They hark back to our neighbors' idolatry. Which He abhors. I can only assume He didn't want to abruptly discontinue this ingrained ritual because the people wouldn't have understood that.'

Not wanting to offend Juda again, I kept my thoughts to myself. I said, "Do you think the sacrificial ceremony will ever be abolished?"

"You mean, when the time comes, will we be dismissed en masse and the Temple be rented out?" replied Juda, cuttingly. Although well-meant, my words had, nonetheless, gone down the wrong way.

"I can't see into God's realm of thought, Amos, but I'm probably not meant to. He commanded Solomon to build a Temple. Why? So He could 'dwell among the Israelites.'[35] Do you think the Lord was envisaging a temporary accommodation? I don't think so. Your question is subversive. You're calling the Word into question. That Word is the last word and my last word on this subject, too."

I found his answer unsatisfactory and ventured a step further. Later on, it was hard to imagine where I got the courage, since I knew full well this question would touch on a raw nerve.

"I was thinking about another reason why the Lord maintained the ritual sacrifices. Shall I explain?" I continued without waiting for his answer. "It's bold speculation. Man has not only good but also very bad, violent traits. The Lord knows that and takes it into account.[36] I wondered if the slaughter ritual might not be an escape valve."

"For what, Amos?"

"For violence that could otherwise be turned against other people."

My remark was not well received. Juda shifted to the edge of his chair and almost shouted, "You talk about the Lord as if He were your like. It seems to me you're an apple that's fallen too far from the tree of Juda.

Dialectics is fine, but you keep going, always pushing. Debating, debating, always asking questions, sowing doubt, and never arriving at a definitive answer. You're abusing your intellect, young man. All of us seek security, every one of us. And only the Torah can provide you with that. Stop these intellectual acrobatics. Go home and study the Torah, take it literally and learn from it."

"Do you want me to leave?"

"That's not what I meant."

"May I continue for a moment?"

"Yes because, despite everything, you fascinate me. You're a rare species. First, though, I'm going to take a rest. I'll see you again tomorrow."

Juda left the room, shaking his head.

E. IS EXEGESIS MAN'S WORK?

The next evening, I immediately set to. Juda was watching me expectantly, even suspiciously, I felt.

"I've been thinking about yesterday's discussion, Juda. Everything's so cut and dry for you. It's all written in stone. I find more openness in the synagogue. You can hear voices there, debate, sometimes squabbling. The atmosphere there is like a warm bath. I don't get that feeling in the Temple. People are silent there. All you can hear is the wailing of animals in their death throes. What's more, you, the priests, put yourselves between me and the Lord. I'm seeking direct contact.

In the synagogue, I get to know my neighbors. We learn together, study together and pray together. That relaxes me. What's more, we don't just discuss high-flying affairs; we talk about everyday things, too. It's comfortable and cosy."

Juda's response was prickly. "As you say, the Temple isn't 'comfortable and cozy' – I could hear the disdain in his voice – that's not what you go to the Temple for. You go there to pay homage to the Lord. That means internal concentration, not a cozy get-together. The synagogue forges links, you say, which is fine, but it's still no substitute for the Temple service. Togetherness is worldly; devotion is about communing with the Lord.

76

And, when it comes to learning, yes, we are supposed to learn, but that means the Torah and the Torah alone. Learn, internalize, put what you've learned into practice, but keep to the text. The Lord speaks in the Torah. You encounter Him in the Temple. Don't venture into all kinds of interpretations. I called that intellectual acrobatics just now. It's a sign of vanity, bordering on arrogance."

"Is that a veiled reference to the Pharisees?"

"It is, indeed. That's exactly what they do. They think they know what the Lord meant. Smart alecs! We reject that; we find their attitude inappropriate. Are they intimate friends with God, or something? They explain His commandments, in their way. They teach people how to apply those rules in daily life. Again, in their own way. They add all kinds of instructions to the written texts. Who gave them the right? The Lord Himself, they claim. In addition to the written commandments, He also purportedly gave Moses oral clarification. That clarification has presumably been transferred from generation to generation by our wise men. To this day. This so-called Oral Torah is supposed to be as binding as the real Torah. Nonsense, in our view! The Oral Torah is man's work.

Don't get me wrong, boy, we priests don't claim that the sages have been trotting out nonsense through the ages. What we do say is that they gave *their* opinion, not that of the Lord and that their pronouncements are therefore not binding. The Pharisees seem to be promoting the synagogue as an alternative to the Temple, the place where God's spirit abides. It's scandalous!"

"So the rift between you, the priests, and the Pharisees is deep."

"Yes, it's unbridgeable."

"Isn't that rather detrimental to our people? It fractures our religious unity. A split is the last thing we could do with at this point. There are already enough divisive elements."

"True, but you can't forsake principles in favour of current considerations."

"Not even for the survival of our country and our people?"

"Not even then. Maintaining morality prevails above the principle of opportunity."

"I agree with you there, but I see the survival of our people as the underlying principle, not the integrity of our moral code or our legal system, always assuming their integrity *is* at risk. Nothing is higher priority, certainly not a tribal conflict over what the Lord does or doesn't expect of us. That, we will never know. Falling into an unbridgeable chasm can cost you your life."

Juda smiled. "You're a smooth customer, you and your silver tongue. You come here to learn from me, but what you are actually doing is lecturing. I ought to get cross and send you away, but I'm not going to. I even quite like the squabbling. I rarely have such encounters. Have you got another intriguing question up your sleeve?"

"Yes, Juda, I have."

"Okay, but not now. Let me get some rest."

"Tomorrow then?"

"If you are want to." And without another word he let me out.

F. COMPROMISE OR CONFRONTATION?

Yes, I did want to! I was there again the following evening. My self-confidence had grown. Juda let me in with a "Good evening." That was all. It looked as if he had a premonition that I would be on the offensive.

His premonition was right. I started the conversation. "I'd like to get something off my chest. This time, it's not a question but an observation. The way you priests behave is inconsistent. You want it both ways. You don't choose. To me, that doesn't seem like a good example."

Juda looked shocked and flushed. "I don't know what you mean. Clarify that remark."

"Well, you see the Temple as the linchpin of our life of faith.

You tell us the High Priest is the intermediary between our people and the Lord. On the other hand, he collaborates with the occupiers, representatives of a culture that's fundamentally contrary to our own. You priests do the same. Isn't that an unholy alliance?

You don't call on our people to resist Hellenistic influences, to not Hellenize their names, to refrain from participating naked in sporting events and attending plays in which idols and demigods play a major role or to ensure that, in our education, the study of the Torah isn't overshadowed by the study of Greek philosophy, literature, drama and rhetoric. Under King Herod, you allowed the Temple to be given the outward appearance of a Greek temple.

Worse still, a lot of priests even flirt with Hellenism themselves. They imitate the behavior of our Hellenized co-citizens and are not so far removed from the greatest collaborators of them all: the moneyed gentry; those who call themselves aristocrats not because they have so much to give, but because they have so much to spend. Talk about setting a good example!

And there's more. Where's the moral voice of the High Priest? Why isn't he warning us of the rot in our society? We're bitterly divided and, worse still, we denigrate one another: aristocrats the man in the street, city dwellers the country dwellers, the pious the freethinking, the Jews the Samaritans, the free citizens the slaves. The principle of rank has even found its way into priestly circles. The Lord commands us to respect one another. That principle is being sorely strained.

Even at the highest levels, there is corruption, bribery, indifference towards the poor, the orphans, and the widows. These are all things the Lord abhors and I hear no cry of indignation from your side.[37] How can you reconcile that with your function?

What's lacking in my view is the prophet, our common conscience. You've neglected to assume their function. I wonder . . ."

Juda interrupted and began pacing up and down the room.

"Stop your miserable complaining, boy. Did you come here

to call us priests to account? What are you trying to say? Again, who do you think you are?"

"Perhaps I did go a bit too far, Juda. Please forgive me but the subject makes me emotional. I'm worried; I wonder how long the Lord will let us live in this land. Our presence here is conditional, dependent on the extent to which we comply with the obligations of our covenant.[38] Our land, our people and our culture are in the danger zone, Juda. That's the way I see it."

Juda calmed down visibly and went back to his seat.

"I overreacted, too. You're partly right, Amos. We priests are, indeed, failing in our moral guidance. We're too busy making sure the Temple cult maintains its central place. You're wrong, though, when it comes to our political activities. Those are a necessary evil."

"Really necessary?"

"Yes."

"But surely there was a good reason why the Lord insisted that Moses entrust the spiritual leadership of our people to his brother Aaron and his descendants.[39] He evidently foresaw difficulties if worldly and spiritual power came into the same hands."

Juda shook his head. "You misunderstand the situation we have been living in for centuries now. Let me refresh your memory.

In Moses we had a worldly leader. During the first Temple period our kings fulfilled that role. After the Babylonian exile, the situation changed fundamentally. We became vassals of the surrounding superpowers. For hundreds of years. First the Persian Empire, later the Hellenistic rulers in Egypt and Syria, heirs to the Empire of Alexander the Great.[40] They allowed us internal self-governance and put that in the hands of the High Priest and his fellow priests. That was a great blessing. It enabled us to largely maintain our philosophy of life and our way of living. On the other hand, the priesthood was confronted with political issues and had to find solutions that satisfied the then rulers.

The sad paradox is that the real rot set in, once we regained our independence. The Hasmonean rulers also appropriated the High Priesthood. The profane and the sacred turned out not to be compatible. Power politics was the name of the game. Moral obligations were overshadowed. All that remained of the priestly tasks was the Temple cult and far too much attention was paid to that.

King Herod, who succeeded the Hasmonean rulers, went one step further. He hired and fired High Priests at his own discretion. The High Priest became a civil servant who had to dance to the king's tune.

Today's Roman occupiers adopted that practice. The High Priest is now responsible for peace and order in our country. So he has to be involved in politics each and every day. We Jews are only a small group in an overwhelmingly Hellenized world. The essential thing for us priests is to maintain the Temple cult, so that Israel can atone for its sins and renew its relationship with the Lord. So we seek compromise rather than confrontation. For us, national sovereignty takes second place. Accommodating the dominant culture is essential to preventing our downfall. Think before you judge, Amos.

And remember: changes are not necessarily destructive. We can learn a lot from the Greek philosophers. Their ideas could enrich our Teachings. You said so yourself."

"Yes, I did, but that was a generalization. It applies to thinking people, but most people don't have time to think about anything. They leave it to others, such as you, the priests. You're trying to justify your shortcomings. Hellenism is overtaking us like a tidal wave. We've got to brace ourselves not to be washed away. Priests should be warning of this and setting a good example. Commendations of Greek culture don't help, Juda."

Juda looked resigned, or at least I thought so. "We do our best to find the right balance, Amos. Too many concessions do, indeed, mean spiritual suicide, but too few mean political suicide. We're aware of this. The path between collaboration and confrontation is narrow and hard to tread. Show a little sympathy!"

81

"But Juda, surely you could have transferred the internal affairs."

"To whom?"

"A rival!"

"You're being ironical again. Okay, so you mean a Pharisee."

"Exactly."

"Theory, my boy. The occupier wouldn't have accepted that. As I said, the High Priest does have some authority with them. The Pharisees are esteemed amongst the Jews, but not amongst the occupiers. In any case, I doubt you'd find a Pharisee willing to get his hands dirty."

"What I have doubts about, Juda, is whether your way is the right one. I long for and am seeking pure, undiluted Judaism."

"Purity? That's a dream, my boy, you won't find it. Our teachings are too complex for that. Who knows the right proportions for the components? Only the Lord. Besides, every one of us has to deal with the world around us. That inevitably leaves its mark on everything we think and do. A hermit might find the purity you're talking about, but such an existence is highly egocentric. That's not what the Lord is asking of you."

Juda stretched and, after a brief pause, said, "I'm exhausted. I'm ending the conversation there. To be honest, your talk depresses me. Do you have any further questions?"

"Lots. May I?"

"Not now. Leave me in peace for a while. Come back next week. Same day, same time." With that, he left the room, again without a word.

G. LIFE AFTER DEATH?

A week later, I was back in front of Juda's door. He let me in. "Good morning," he said, stiffly. That was all. He offered me a seat. A chair in front of his desk, rather than the divan, like the other evenings. He evidently wished to keep his distance.

His expression was harsh and he opened the conversation with, "Have you come to ask something or to lecture?"

I realized I'd gone too far the previous week. "Juda, I hold you in high regard, I assure you. I'm the student, albeit a rather outspoken one."

"Excessively outspoken, if you ask me. But let's get down to business. What else is bothering you?" There was an acid tone to his voice.

"It's a question that weighs heavily on me," I muttered and, after a short pause, "What happens after death?"

"To you?"

"To us."

"Are you afraid of death?"

"I'm afraid of uncertainty. What will happen to me?"

"Ah, I seem to hear the voice of the Pharisee in the background again," remarked Juda, ironically. "What's he been putting into your head now?"

"Nothing. He gave his opinion. He didn't impose it."

"Did he tell you man is actually immortal? In the first instance, his soul? And that the dead will later be physically resurrected? Did he talk about a heavenly court the resurrected have to appear before and did he announce that a heavenly future awaits the just and sinners can expect their rightful punishment?"

"There are Pharisees who claim that."

"Well, do you know what I think about it? To put it bluntly, it's pure nonsense.[41] The idea defies the reason with which man is blessed."

"Isn't that going too far, Juda? How can you be so adamant?"

"Look around you, young man. Living matter decays, it's inevitable. That process is irreversible. We're made from dust and to dust we return. The Lord animates that dust. That means we're offered the opportunity to gradually give our life a strictly personal stamp. That stamp is our soul. The soul isn't a thing. It's a dye, as it were, that permeates and colors our whole body, our whole existence. That soul has no independence. A flower – the

83

soul – can't exist without its stalk, the body; or music without the instrument that produces it. To put it irreverently, we die lock, stock and barrel. All that remains is a memory, nothing more. We don't live forever, we sleep forever, surrounded by absolute silence. That idea reassures me. An immortal soul! What an absurd idea, Amos." Juda got up and began to pace.

"The soul makes you what you are: Amos the doubter, the seeker, a unique product. There will never by anyone like you once you're gone. Imagine the soul were immortal; it would never be able to find another suitable body and would die from misery."

He paused. "You look disappointed. Had you expected a different answer?"

"Not expected, no, but I had hoped. Death as absolutely nothing. That idea scares me. Do you, as a priest, have the right to deny people the hope of a coming world, of an *Olam Haba* (Hebrew)?"

"Should we give them false hope, then?"

"Are you sure that hope is false?"

"Of course not. No one can be sure. But I'm convinced it is!"

"Why discourage people, though, Juda. Let them think; let them dream; as far as I'm concerned you can leave them under the delusion that they'll be rewarded for their earthly deeds or punished for any misdemeanours. The first idea gives them hope and the second delivers them from evil."

"I disagree with you, Amos. Seek the Lord on earth, not in all kinds of heavenly fantasies. See Him in what you do, in the dedication with which you do it, in the gratitude of people you do it for, in the good feeling that gives you. Seek Him in what you leave behind when you're gone. The internalized Torah must be your compass, not fantasies about any heavenly court."

"You're expecting rather a lot from people."

"It's not I, but the Lord who sets the bar high, at the level of the Sinai Covenant."

84

"But Juda, what happens to all those wretches who escape their just desserts here on earth?"

"If our people sins, then we are punished, here on earth. Did you think it was a coincidence that we've lost our independence? The Lord regularly punishes our people. He'll never forsake us, though."

"My question was about the individual, Juda, the sinner who escapes his punishment here on earth, not our people."

"How do you know if he escapes it? You can't see into his conscience. Guilty feelings can be a heavy punishment."

"Perhaps so, Juda, but that answer doesn't convince me. It's just that so many people in our society, through no fault of their own, are in such difficulties while others, often undeservedly, wallow in luxury. I can't understand how the Lord can allow that."[42]

"That's not His fault; it's ours. He gave us clear guidelines on how to live. If we ignore them, then that's our business, not His."

"I still have hope, though, Juda!"

"Hope of what?"

"The existence of immortality."

"I'll say it again: that's an unreasonable idea."

"Reason can fall short, Juda."

"That's enough, boy. You're cultivating your doubt to demonstrate how much reason you yourself possess. Vanity! If you over-concentrate your doubt, it can become toxic. Take care."

Juda yawned again, whether from boredom, irritation or fatigue I couldn't tell. "I'd like to leave it there," he sighed. "I'll give you one more evening and a limit of two questions and then I'm stopping. You're exhausting me."

"Tomorrow evening?"

"Okay." There followed a pause. "You've got guts, young man. You dare to say what you're thinking. I appreciate that, but don't get too reckless."

He banged the door shut behind me.

H. ARE WE THE EVIL?

Twenty-four hours later. I was standing on Juda's doorstep again. He opened the door and, this time, made an inviting gesture, seemingly in a good mood.

"Ah, here's our know-all again," he laughed, "The boy has come to teach the priests a lesson."

"With your permission, Juda, the boy who wants to learn but won't swallow everything hook, line and sinker."

"Take care, Amos. Questions can conceal criticism. You're entitled to criticize, at least as far as I'm concerned, but not everybody feels the same. Don't forget that. Now, your question."

I hesitated. I wanted some clarification of God's policy. Perhaps Juda might, again, see such a question as impertinence. I asked my question anyway.

"Who controls my life; the Almighty or me, myself?"

"Where did that come from? Your questions really stretch the bounds of reason."

"What prompted it, Juda, was a chance meeting I had near the Temple. There was a man standing there with his eyes on the Temple, praying. I could understand what he was saying and it shocked me. 'May the Temple soon disappear. The Lord has abandoned this place and now curses it.'

I spoke to the man. I said, 'You're a God denier. Go away. You've got no business being here.'

'You're mistaken, sir,' he replied, 'I hold the Lord in high esteem. I follow His way, the only true way.'

'The only true way, you say. Can you describe that path for me?'

'No, I'm not allowed to. I'm an Essene, a member of the community that lives in Qumran. The true path is only revealed to those who are found worthy of joining our group.'

'So, if I've understand correctly, you believe you're a privileged person?'

'Yes, you've understood correctly.'

86

'Have you lived such a virtuous life, then?'

'Well, I've done my best, but that's not the point. It was predestined.'

'Predestined? By whom?'

'By the Lord Himself; he decided long before I was born how my life would be.'

I couldn't believe my ears.

'I don't understand what you mean, sir. So are we some kind of puppets in God's hands, not responsible for what we do or don't do?'

There was no reply. The man went into a house and hurried up the stairs.

Have you got an answer, Juda?"

"I know what he meant. The Jews in the Qumran community do believe the Lord has predestined everything in our lives. Before you're even born, He decides whether you'll be one of the 'Children of the Light' – the righteous – or the 'Children of the Darkness,' the damned.[43] I have no affinity whatsoever with those ideas; in fact, I see them as an absurdity. I can't imagine how they came by them. A manifestation of God's omnipotence? But that attitude would be entirely contrary to what Moses taught us in His name. We're created in God's image. He guides; He's not guided. So, by definition, we can't be puppets. We've been created as free people, tasked with building our own lives. We, ourselves, are responsible for the final product and we can't pass the buck, not to our parents, not to our teachers, not to the Lord 'who made me like that.'[44] The Lord doesn't control people.

Moreover, the Essenes cherish the arrogant but crazy idea that the Lord has predestined them and only them for an eternal, blissful life."[45]

"Where do people get such ideas, Juda?"

"As I said, I have no idea, son; one can only guess. It could be that they're scared of the unknown in our life; that they need security, and life simply doesn't offer them that. The idea of providence, preferably offered by the supernatural, provides security. And, as I said, their way of thinking also unmistakably entails a considerable level of arrogance. They claim the Lord has chosen them. They look down on outsiders. Unfortunately, people seem to have a need to feel superior to others, to give themselves delusions of grandeur by walking over other people. Does the Qumran community have any reason to confer itself a preferential position? None that I know of."

"So predestination is a fantasy product of human need."

"That's the way I see it. I'd even go a step further. I find that product not only absurd, I actually find it repugnant. Why, you might ask. Because, unfortunately, there are still plenty of people making mischief on this earth. Is that predestined by the Lord? Of course it isn't. Is the Lord wicked? Well, remember what Moses taught us:[46]

"A faithful God – never unjust – righteous and upright is He."

"Man has wicked traits. They sometimes get the better of him. Wickedness comes from man."[47]

"But the Lord did make him that way."

"No, my boy, that's a misrepresentation of the facts. He gave man the capacity to do good or evil. Man himself decides which path to take. Again, not the Lord."

"For once, I can't contradict you there. Your words reassure me. I don't like the idea of our lives being lived for us, being steered by someone else, even if that someone else is the Lord. That would make my life pointless, insignificant."

Juda nodded in agreement and yawned again.

"I can see you've had enough."

"No, Amos, not yet. I'm just tired. I'm an old man."

"But you allowed me one last question."

"I did, indeed. And I'll keep my word. I expect you to do likewise."

"Yes, I promise, even if reluctantly."

1. THEM OR US?

"I'd like to get on to our last topic. Just now, you said, 'the Lord isn't wicked. He's the prototype of the contrary. It's for that very reason that He's become my hero, Juda, the being that fights against injustice and raises the downtrodden. So I don't understand why, several times, He has called on us to entirely destroy an aggressor, women and children included. King Saul, for example, was given such a task when he fought against the Amalekites.[48] He didn't carry out the order in full and the Lord rejected him. A terrible punishment. I can't reconcile such orders with His repeated encouragement to love our neighbors, including foreigners."[49]

"I understand your doubts, Amos, but don't forget, first and foremost, that the Lord didn't command us to love our enemies. Aside from that, wars are simply fought on the cutting edge. It's them or us.

The Lord chose us as a vanguard to achieve His vision of a new world. A world based on law and justice, where everyone is valued, regardless of their antecedents. That's the essence of the Sinai Covenant. That's a thorn in the side for plenty of rulers in this world. They'd like to see our people wiped from the face of the earth. If at first they don't succeed, they'll keep trying until they do. That confronts the Lord with a gigantic ethical dilemma. Act mercilessly or allow His people to be wiped out. He chooses the first option, reluctantly, one assumes.

Don't forget, either, that surrounding peoples are not bound to any ethical code comparable to ours. Vanquished opponents are devoured. It's a question of eat or be eaten. The Lord had good reason for giving the orders that bother you so much."

"Isn't our code of conduct binding under all circumstances, then, Juda?"

"No, my boy, not under all circumstances. Their applicability is not independent of the time and culture we live in. Sometimes we're forced to content ourselves with a compromise. Remember that if the wolf has unlimited freedom the sheep no longer has any life, and if the sheep has unlimited freedom the wolf has to be held prisoner. Both have to relinquish some level of freedom because both have the right to exist."

"I do understand you, Juda, but we haven't always stuck to the golden mean. Evidently the Lord hasn't, either."

"You're right. The Lord may be almighty, but He isn't necessarily infallible in His judgement. He sometimes makes mistakes. Don't forget: the creation of the world was a first and man turned out to be a capricious, often unpredictable creature. Even the Almighty can occasionally make rash decisions."

"Now you're talking like His chamberlain," I laughed.

"Not His chamberlain," Juda shook his head, "But a paladin, someone who'd go through fire for Him."

"To become a martyr?"

"If His name were really to be profaned, yes."

"I don't think He'd be very pleased with that: one more champion down. Anyway, far be it for me to speak for the Lord.

I've found this discussion – our last, unless I'm mistaken – extremely informative. You're far more of a relativist than I imagined. You're not the first I've met. I've come to the conclusion that I'm allowed to relativize, too. But when it comes to our moral code I don't. I attempt to avoid moral compromises as much as possible."

"That's to your credit, my boy. But you'd better go now. I've already given you too much time. I'm worn out."

He shook me by the hand and let me out. "You're a pest, Amos, but you're fascinating. I'll give you two more pieces of advice to take away with you.

Don't make things too difficult for yourself. Take life as it comes, take things as they are. Not every question has an answer, a clear answer. There are often several possible responses to a question. Learn to live with that. Relativism is, indeed, a precious commodity.

I'm saying this to you as Juda, the person. In our discussions,

I spoke to you as Juda the priest and he doesn't indulge much in relativism. He doesn't allow himself that. He isn't allowed that. Juda the person has a different stance in life.

The second piece of advice is this. You have the tendency to inflate yourself. You don't need to. You're a sensible person; that much is clear. Be humble! Even the king, says the Lord, may not imagine that he is better than others and, in any respect, above the law.[50] Moses, our greatest leader ever, was humble: 'more humble than anyone else on the face of the earth.'[51] The Lord himself is humble. He has never called Himself almighty or omniscient. Take that to heart. Humility is a virtue.

But now you'd better go. Farewell, Amos."

"Thank you for all the time you've been willing to spend with me."

He waved me off.

J. REFLECTION

I walked back home. A fine man, that Juda, I thought. Far less of a stick in the mud than I'd thought. It was certainly quite an honor to have been taken into his confidence.

I didn't get home until late. My father was waiting up for me. "I'm worried, son; you've been so restless recently. Have your conversations with Juda gotten you any further?"

"To some extent, Father. They've given me insight into the way our priests think. I didn't get an answer to the question of how I should interpret the predicate of 'Jew,' though. Perhaps I didn't ask the right questions. Besides that, he puts things into perspective far more than I'd expected from a high-ranking priest."

My father put his arm around me. "You make me proud, son. Even now, before you have even achieved anything. You're asking a key question. Am I content with the person I am? You're questioning the carat of your identity, but you're jumping the gun. You're not yet you; you're still becoming you. Identity is something you gradually form. Over the course of time, your profile becomes clearer, more sharply outlined. It's like a wall painting or a mosaic. The maker builds it up, brush-stroke by brush-stroke, tile by tile. At first, the likeness is still crude, not yet clearly recognizable, but it gradually becomes clearer, more refined, at least if the artist continues working at it. Alternatively, he might break off prematurely. A work of art is never really completed. Neither is an identity. All being well, you work on it your whole life, although many people don't get that far.

Keep seeking, but don't expect to find ready-made answers. If I can draw on the imagery we used just now, you'll find paints, mosaic tiles, in different hues. You'll have to build up the work of art – your identity, in other words – yourself. But remember this. Your design is based on a foundation, a wall, a floor, metaphorically speaking. You received that foundation from your parents. You're a Jew, a Judean. That's the foundation on which your identity must rest. There's no hurry, son. The only deadline is death."

"Well, I'm setting off tomorrow, Father, and I'll try and bear your words in mind."

"May I ask where you're going?"

"To Modi'in, Father, to your old friend David."

"Ah, he'll be a tough nut to crack. Brace yourself, son, and a blessing on your head."

CHAPTER 4

DAVID, A ZEALOT

The Torah is invincible; we're not.

Crush the heads of hostile rulers . . . Show mercy to the people
called by your name: Israel, whom you named your firstborn.
The Wisdom of Ben Sira 36:12, 14

A.   TO BATTLE! THE LORD IS WITH US.

I was on my way to Modi'in, a town roughly 25 km to the north-
west of Jerusalem. I wanted to talk to a man who, in his youth,
had worked with my father on building the Port of Caesarea.
His name was David. According to my father, at that time he'd
been a staunch radical nationalist. I was curious to know whether
he still was.

The journey took me two days. After some searching, I found
his house – a little cottage. Quite different from Judah's residence. I knocked. An old, rather worn-looking man opened the
door.

"Who are you?" he asked.

"My name's Amos. I'm the son of Mordechai from Jerusalem.
He used to be a stonemason but now he's a silversmith. You
worked with him in Caesarea in the past."

"Well, at least you come with good credentials. I hope you
haven't come to tell me he's dead?"

"No, fortunately I haven't."

"Well, come on in. What are you doing here, then?"

I got straight to the point. "I'd like to hear your opinion on the situation in our country. You're going to ask me why. My answer is, because I'm seriously worried. We've lost our independence for the second time in less than a hundred years[77] and we've become a vassal of the mighty Roman Empire. How long will that empire last? Are there any counter forces? Will Judea survive, or will it be erased from history, merging with the province of Syria to which the Romans have linked our country? Will our people, which should have been a holy people, relapse into idolatry?"[78]

David looked me straight in the eye. "You're asking dangerous questions, young man. You're very open about your politics. The government doesn't much like this kind of talk and there are informers knocking around these days. I hope you're not trying to catch me out."

"No, you can trust me. I'm not trying to trap you, I'm just trying to elicit a response. I'm curious to know your opinion. What kind of attitude should a Jew have towards the government in our times? Resist? Or collaborate in order to 'prevent worse,' as they say."

"Well, what do you think, son?"

"What should our attitude be, you ask. Well, isn't it obvious? Here you are in Modi'in, where the Maccabean revolt started against the Syrian oppressors.[79] A fight for freedom against a powerful enemy, whom we ultimately beat. A wonderful example of how a passionate minority can vanquish a major force. Passion is a powerful weapon."

"What do you mean by a passionate minority?"

"A group that believes in its cause, which is convinced the Lord is on its side. Together with Him, we can literally move mountains."

"If I understand you rightly, then you're calling for active resistance against the Romans."

"Correct."

Fig. 5 At the end of the Jewish War (67–70 CE), after the conquest, the Roman commander Titus took the golden Menorah from the Temple in Jerusalem to Rome, where it was displayed in the triumphal arch constructed in his honor in the Roman Forum.
From: Kedourie, E. (Ed) (1979). *The Jewish world. History and culture of the Jewish people*. New York: Harry. N. Abrams, Publishers.

This war, partly provoked by the zealots, was strongly religiously inspired but was to lead to a catastrophe: the end of the Jewish kingdom of Judah.

"Do I also gather that you think the Lord will actively support us?"

"Correct again. *He* is our king. There is no other."

"Isn't that rather wishful thinking? It all sounds rather arrogant."

"What do you mean? Did you think the Lord would ever let us down? His quartermasters? Not give us the strength to stand up again when we're beaten and finally triumph?"

"Do you mean militarily?"

"Yes, I do." David was getting visibly agitated. He looked ready to take up his sword and go off to battle. He is certainly passionate, person I thought to myself.

"Have you forgotten that our presence in this land is conditional, depending on our behavior, which can't have been much to the Lord's liking the past few years."[80]

"That may be so, Amos, but can you see anyone taking our place? Could the Egyptians take over our mission? The Romans, the Franks, the Germans? Can you see that happening? No you can't. The Lord will realize that, too. We make mistakes, yes, but once we're aware of them we try and improve our lives. The Lord has always proved willing to forgive His "treasured possession."[81] That willingness won't go away. I'm convinced of that.

And there's something else I'm convinced of, Amos. The Lord demands that we stand up *now* to a power that enchains us, to a culture that threatens to suffocate us, to the collaborators who collude with the oppressors, to the defectors. That's what He demands of us *now*. That's the condition *now* for us remaining in this land. Not passivity, not waiting until He does something, but action. The time when the Lord led us by the hand is over. We've become a mature people. We've got to take care of our own business. The Lord will only intervene if things threaten to go wrong."

"But, David, remember what happened just after the death of King Herod, just a few years ago? We rose against the Roman regime and Varus crushed us mercilessly. Thousands of our people were crucified and even more carried off as slaves."[82]

"Do you think I've forgotten that, boy? No, I was in the thick of the fighting. And has it made me think any differently? No! My mates died for a good cause. That sweetens death."

"A fairy tale, David. Such a death might be sweet, but dying like that is agony. Besides, how do you imagine that we, a mouse without a standing army, can take on a lion, a world power with an illustrious fighting force? It's bound to end badly. The Lord isn't a military commander, an arms supplier or a strategy."

"He's all that and much more. He can make a mouse into a formidable opponent. As long as that mouse has enough passion. Didn't Gideon succeed in vanquishing the forces of the Midianites and the Amalekites with just a handful of men?[83] Didn't Judas Maccabeus and his followers defeat the Syrian rulers, retake Jerusalem and cleanse and rededicate the Temple?[84] Didn't Judas' brothers succeed in turning us into an independent state after years of struggle? Passion – the conviction that you're fighting for a good cause – it's an almighty weapon. Especially when that conviction rests on God's word."

"But does it actually rest on God's word in your case? I understood from the prophet Zechariah that the Lord shuns armed violence. If He comes to the aid of man, it's with His spirit: "not by might nor by power, but by my Spirit."[85] His spirit is embedded in the Torah and we familiarize ourselves with it by studying the Torah. That's the way I see it. The Torah is invincible; we're not. As long as that work determines our defense strategy, the survival of our people is guaranteed.

What do you think of my interpretation?"

"Fine words, young man, but actions speak louder than words! The Torah isn't a cocoon to which you can safely retreat. That would be cowardly. That wouldn't please the Lord. The scriptures call us to action. "Don't wait passively. Defend what I stand for; defend My Word, My principles." Doesn't He, Himself, set a good example? He's a courageous Being. Hasn't He dealt with His competitors and enemies in this world for good?"

"That last remark isn't true, David; now it's you doing the wishful thinking. You know as well as I do that, in our world, idolatry is still alive and kicking, that God's deniers still raise their heads. There's still plenty work for Him to do."

"Quite right, young man. For him *and* for us. It's urgent that we stop patiently suffering and actively intervene."

"Openly revolt."

"Yes, a thousand times yes. Do I have to shout it out? I was an active propagandist in my youth. I tried recruiting people to our cause. I was a member of a guerrilla group, I single-handedly killed Roman soldiers and collaborators. I'm not strong enough for that any longer, but my views haven't changed."

"And what did all that achieve? Nothing! Roman rule has simply become increasingly unbearable."

"Well that's not our fault; you can't blame it on the zealots. You can blame it on those characters who call themselves the freedom party, who plead for moderation, compromises, accommodation. The more we concede, the more the Romans demand. They know how to handle softies. The peace doves don't realize that. Our group is still small, too small, we're unable to offer enough counterweight. I'm afraid the Lord will be disappointed and start wondering whether anything will ever come of our mission like this. He knows the way to the *Sheol* (Hebrew) is paved with soft soap.[86] Many of our Pharisee brothers say to us, 'Save the struggle until the Messiah has come.' We say, 'We mustn't wait for the coming of the Messiah; the Messiah is waiting for us.' Excuse me for a moment, Amos, old men sometimes have trouble with their waterworks."

After a couple of minutes, David came back. The conversation had wound me up too far to continue straight away. "I'm sorry, David," I said, "Now you will have to excuse me for a moment. Young men also have trouble holding their water." I had no such trouble, but I had to compose myself for a moment. I'd almost had an emotional outburst against David, but I'd managed to restrain myself. What an aggressive person, I thought. A dangerous man. He's asking for passion. He's got it in abundance, but it's directed wrongly, not at our preservation but at our downfall. A total lack of realism. How can we keep a check on the likes of him? Ideas aren't fleeting wisps of thought that quickly disperse. On the contrary: ideas can mobilize the masses, cause spiritual earthquakes that can ultimately turn out be victorious or catastrophic.

I went back into David's living room and sat down again.

B.   IS THE LORD WITH US?

"Do you agree with me, boy?" David began. My blood was up and I wasn't about to soft soap him, to use his words.

"No, David, I certainly don't! Your ideas could have catastrophic consequences. Suppose we openly revolt and it turns out the Lord isn't with us, that he feels we acted imprudently and rashly.

Suppose the Romans make mincemeat of us. Suppose Judea is destroyed, Jerusalem and our Temple razed to the ground, the Temple ransacked, great numbers of our people killed and even more carried off to Rome as slaves. For me, that's a nightmare, a spectre, but when I listen to you that just becomes a concrete reality. You're asking if I agree with you? Frankly, your ideas terrify me!"

I thought I saw a look of pity cross David's face.

"I trust the Lord won't think like that but, rather, the other way around. I suspect He will be disappointed if we give in and don't fight back. He thought He had created beings with some backbone.

Fear, young man, is a fast track to cowardice. Giving in, subjugating yourself until nothing remains of your own identity, that's what scares me."

"I do admire courage, David, but overconfidence makes me

99

nervous. Have you zealots learnt nothing from our history?[87] The northern kingdom of Israel succumbed in a foolhardy war against the then superpower of Assyria, and Judea was destroyed in an improvident battle against the Babylonians, the rulers of their day."

"Yes, of course, but remember that Judea rose again from its ashes and a large part of what was then Israel was reconquered by our kings John Hyrcanus and Aristobulus I.[88] To put it rather lightly: All's well that ends well."

"Rubbish, David, there's no 'ends well' about it. After the inglorious end of the Hasmonean dynasty, Rome forced Herod down our throats as king and he was certainly no devout Pharisee. His son and heir Achelaus was a complete disaster. He was deposed by Rome and it's he who is responsible for the deplorable condition our land is in right now. Nothing ended well; the end was miserable."[89]

"So what you're actually saying is: we've messed things up with the Lord once again. I can agree with you there. He's punishing us but, I repeat, it turns out time after time that he never drops us entirely; sooner or later he raises us up again."

"All too often later, though, David, much, much later. By that time, we've already been through a great deal of calamity. What you and your associates have in mind could ultimately mean the end of the Jewish land. I assume God's patience does have its bounds."

"I don't think so, but even if it does then I'll accept that. Better to be dead than a slave. Better to disappear from history than to go down in it as a lowly wanderer, homeless, dependent on a host, benevolent or otherwise, who all too often looks down his nose at you. Why? Because, as of old, that wanderer has allowed himself to be thrown out of the window by the conquerors like so much refuse. Never that."

He emphasized his final words by stamping his foot on the ground.

"You'd rather fight to the death, then."

"Yes, I would."

"Do you think deep, or not so deep, in your heart that this sanctifies God's name?"[90]

"Yes, I do, but I also have the honor of demonstrating that Jews can wield not only words but also a sword."

"Evidently, you're seeking martyrdom. I get the feeling you're longing to die for what you see as the interests of your people, your country and the honor of the Almighty. You think this will compensate for the mistakes our people have made over the years."

"You've got it."

"But you haven't, David. I can't imagine the Lord supports your plans. From a human perspective, He will find them reckless, rash, irresponsible. If your plans are carried out, that could be a good reason for Him to withdraw His hand from us for good."

"That may be so but – I'll say it again – we'll then go down in history as a heroic people, who fought to the death for an idea, an idea with a divine signature."

"I don't believe you're following the Lord's path like this. Whether His choice was right or not, He chose us as His vanguard on the way to a better world. We mustn't jeopardise that mission. That would be a real desecration of God's name. You're probably thinking that one day you'll be rewarded by the Lord for what you brand as valour."

"Not at all. Although some of my kindred spirits might. I don't believe all that nonsense about an *Olam Haba* (Hebrew), a coming world. That's just fables the Pharisees bandy around to reassure all the deprived people in our land. Later, once you're dead, you'll be generously compensated. Fodder for the gullible!

But what am I going on about? I'm sitting here defending myself to a young man who turns up wanting to know my opinion and, in fact, does nothing but wrap me over the knuckles."

"I'm sorry I've annoyed you so much, but please understand. I did, indeed, come here for information on your political insight but, in my opinion, your ideas are so dangerous that I have to refute them. I've got nothing against you personally, but I do have something against your vision of the future."

"That's no excuse. The two go together. But now one question for you and one answer from me and then I'll have to ask you to leave. So what's your vision of the future?"

I reflected for a while. "That's a difficult question, David. I'm neither a soothsaying nor a prophet, but let me say this: I can think of a form of resistance other than physical violence."

"And what might that be, Amos? I hope you're not going to start playing the pious Pharisee. Please spare me that."

"I won't spare you that! What I think is that we have to persevere, to persist, whatever happens, in order to have faith."

"Faith in whom?"

"Like you, in the Lord, who else? But in a different way. Empires have fallen one after another. We exist and we will continue to exist."

"If managing to survive is your only strategy, then I wouldn't be so sure of it."

"Not just surviving. Surviving in an impregnable bastion, which you so condescendingly called a 'cocoon:' our Holy Scriptures. Are they a 'cocoon'? Far from it. In fact, they call to action. Wherever you are – children of Abraham – in Judea or in the diaspora, try to realize what, according to Moses, the Lord was envisaging. A society based on law and justice, tempered by compassion, which guarantees equal rights for all men and cares for the underprivileged in society, a society prepared to beat its swords into ploughshares and its spears into pruning-hooks.[91] Start with yourself. Set a good example."

"Lofty words, Amos. But you're kidding yourself again. Men are no angels. What you're saying, in fact, is: throw in the towel. Sit and wait in your cocoon. Turn our land, wherever it might be, into one big yeshiva.[92] I can't bear the idea. It would suffocate me. It would stifle our people. I want to be able to go about freely, say what I have to say, contradict, be able to call others to account. I want to be a Jew without being ashamed of being Jewish, one who cherishes his identity."

"I feel the same need, David, and it's not currently being satisfied but, believe me, things could be far worse. We could be persecuted, become dependent on malicious rulers, turned into the laughing stock of our fellow citizens. Then that yeshiva will be your only refuge. And, incidentally, from that point of view I'm not thinking about a yeshiva; I'm thinking about a synagogue. That's our mobile Temple. We can set it up anywhere. Then we can be ourselves wherever we are. You're hoping the Lord will be with you and yours. Remember that He is only to be found in that 'cocoon.'"

David shook his head. "You're not suited to our camp. Our paths diverge too widely. I want to keep respect for my people and for myself, hold my head up high. You're prepared to bow your head; to buy peace and pay with self-respect. In the worst case, you'll become a yes man."

"I would define that divergence differently, David. For me, the existence of our people goes before everything. Yes, I'm paying for that, it's true. But the price isn't self-respect; it's self-development. It'll be impossible to realize certain potentials. The price is certainly high, but the yield – our continued existence – is higher."

David stood up and opened the front door. "Our ways part. Metaphorically, but also literally. I'm going upstairs and you're going back home. Give my greetings to your father. Have a good journey."

He shook my hand and shut the door behind me with a bang.

C.   REFLECTION

I was surprised. Surprised at David. What an internal fury; what a lack of doubt. I was surprised at myself, as well. I, too, had spoken with such conviction, allowed myself to be provoked by David's self-assuredness, adopted standpoints of which I was far from certain. Do we really have to fight, or should we be throwing in the towel? Does fighting offer the only chance of success? Does the synagogue actually offer a survival strategy in case – God forbid – we should lose our land? Will our people not then be discouraged and lose its way? These are questions to which I actually have no answer. With David, I pretended to be the man I would, in fact, have liked to be. It was a deceptive façade.

I arrived home exhausted. "And?" enquired my father, "What did you think of David?"

"Well now, what did I think of him? A passionate man, Father, that's for sure, but a fanatic, an extremist driven by fury rather than ideals. He scared me. Not the man himself but his notions. If it were up to him, we would be standing up against the Romans as soon as possible."

"You don't surprise me, son, as a young man he was already a hothead. And he's not the only one in this day and age. There's a whole group like him. They call themselves Zealots. Their motto is: 'No king besides the Lord.' They reject all existing political bodies. I don't understand how society could function like that. Is the Lord some kind of super administrator? Anyway, they're playing a dangerous game and they could plunge our land into an adventure without prospects in the expectation that the Lord will dig us out of trouble. It's a bold assumption. We stand on our own two feet and we're held responsible for our acts and omissions. I don't like extremes and I've always steered clear from them.

There's another group that I consider to be extremists, religious rather than nationalist. They live apart from our society in Qumran, a settlement on the west side of the Dead Sea.

I won't tell you anything about them. I advise you to seek them out and see for yourself. I don't know anyone there, so you'll have to find your own way."

"You're a wonderful person, Father. You manage to steer without taking the helm."

I rested for two days and then travelled eastwards into the desert of Judea, towards the Dead Sea, curious as to what awaited me.

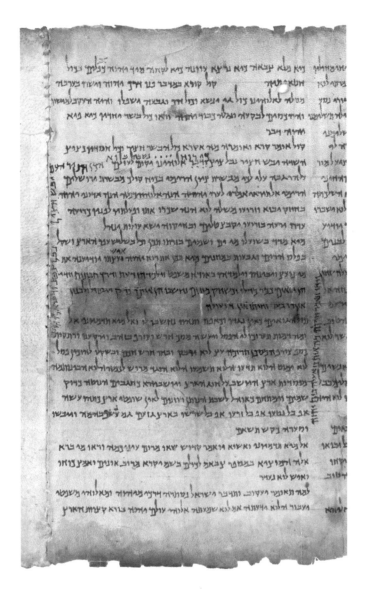

Fig. 6 Part of the Isaiah scroll. (Isaiah 40:2 to 40:28), found in one of the caves near Qumram. It is the only book of the Bible of which a complete text has been found in Qumran.
From: Jong de, M. & Dorp de, J. (Red) (2013). *Qumram en de Bijbel. Over ontstaan, overlevering en vertaling van de Bijbel.* [Qumran and the Bible. On the origins, tradition and translation of the Bible] Heerenveen: Jongbloed.

CHAPTER 5

ELI, A PROMINENT MEMBER
OF THE QUMRAN COMMUNITY

The question is not what you make of the Lord, but what the Lord makes of you.

If you have been foolish enough to be arrogant and plan evil, stop and think!

Proverbs 30:32

A. GOD'S PREHISTORY

The next day, after gleaning some information on how to reach Qumran, I set off.[93] It was a long, difficult journey straight through a barren, burning desert; uphill, downhill, with a water supply that was running out. Spiritually, I became calm. My body was demanding all my attention. When I arrived at the Dead Sea, a shepherd pointed the way to Qumran.

I was exhausted by the time I got there. The settlement seemed to be a closed stronghold. I knocked. No one answered. I banged long and hard on the door with my stick. Finally, an old man opened up. He was as wrinkled as an overripe olive and looked at me dispassionately.

"What do you want?" he asked "Who are you?"

"I'm Amos, the son of Mordechai, a silversmith from Jerusalem."

"Are you indeed? From Jerusalem, eh?"

"Yes, that's what I said."

He hawked and spat on the ground. "People from Jerusalem aren't welcome here."

"What are you saying? Will you leave someone from your own people outside, even if he knocks exhausted at the door?"

"As far as we're concerned, you're undesirable strangers."

"Excuse me, but I don't understand what you're saying; if that is so then have you forgotten that the Lord instructed us to love our neighbors, including strangers?"[94]

"Not our enemies. For us, Jerusalem and everything to do with it has become besmirched with lies. Literally everything: the Temple, the priesthood – especially the High Priest – the Sacrificial Ceremony. Everything! We've left it all behind us. We – our group – and only we, have followed in God's footsteps. He has chosen us. We are the 'Children of the Light.'"[95]

I couldn't believe my ears. "I still can't understand what you're saying. I'd very much like to hear more about it, but above all I'm hungry and unbearably thirsty. Do you also see someone in need as an undesirable stranger, or may I come in?"

"Wait there a moment, I'll go and see."

He closed the door again. I was there for a long time. Eventually, the man reappeared.

"You may come in. You can take a couple of days to regain your strength and speak with one of our elders. It's a great honor. I've said you seem sensible and respectable.

After that, you'll have to leave unless you're prepared to consider joining our community. Be aware, though; that would be a big step for you. A step that can take years. But you'll hear all about that."

I went inside and was led through a big, bare space with wooden tables and benches along the walls to a small, spartan room with the same kind of table and one chair on each side.

"Wait here, Amos. Someone will join you in a moment. In the meantime, I'll get you something to eat and drink. You look as if you could do with it."

After a long wait, a man did come in, a stocky man with a full beard. He gave me a surly look. "So, young man, what are you doing here, apart from eating and drinking?"

"Much more. May I ask your name first?"

"Elijahu. They call me Eli. I'm one of the leaders of this community. I repeat, what have you come here for?"

"I'd like to know something about the views within your community. You lead such an isolated life. Strange stories are doing the rounds in Jerusalem about you."

"Something about our views, you say. Well, that's rather a broad question. Could you be slightly more specific?"

"What I want to know, Eli, is how a Jew should live and think to be a real Jew. I've been looking for answers."

"Well, Jerusalem can't give you any answers to those questions. You do, indeed, need to be here. Be more precise in your question, though."

I hesitated for a moment and decided to swallow hard and get down to brass tacks. The swallowing would probably be harder for him, though.

"Don't be alarmed, Eli: my first point is that I don't know what to make of the Lord." Eli's face was a picture of amazement.

"You don't know what to make of the Lord? Well, that's quite a presumptuous remark! The question is not what you should make of the Lord but what the Lord should make of you. You're either a prospective sage, contaminated with Hellenistic ideas, or a fool or a rascal."

"None of the three, Eli. I'm a drifter, lost in the maze of opinions that we Jews have made of our Teachings."

"An apparent maze. There is only one interpretation and that's been formulated by the Teacher of Righteousness.[96] You ask what you should make of the Lord, but you shouldn't be asking; you should be studying and acting. Do what He asks of you."

"But who is that He, Eli? That's the question that's been haunting me. I can't just do. I ask questions. Seek answers. Only once I've found them can I start doing."

"That He is the Creator of everything there is."

"That's a standard response, Eli, and it's not enough for me. What was there before that time?"

"Chaos."

"So He created order."

"Yes, He did."

"In the material world, but not in our spiritual existence. That's a world without cohesion, with a chaotic churning of opinions."

"It's your so-called teachers, the Pharisees, who've made a chaos of God's directives. They interpret away, believing they're all authorized to have an opinion. As if the Lord authorized them. Nonsense! The result is chaos. There's only one authorized representative and that's the Teacher of Righteousness, our leader."

"Are you the initiates?"

"What do you mean, Amos?'

"You're the only ones the correct interpretation of God's word has been revealed to, aren't you? So you see yourselves as God's true priests."

"You understand me well, young man."

"May I continue, Eli, or do you find my questions too simple?"

"That, they're not. They're not asked often enough. Go on."

"What state was the earth in before the Lord intervened?"

"The earth was without form and void."

"I've read that in the Genesis scripture, but that formulation is unclear to me. An unformed mass can be formed, but not a void. There's nothing to form."

"None of your semantic acrobatics, young man. I don't like them. Read 'chaos and waste'[97]then, rather than 'without form and void.'"[98]

"Now you're playing word games, too, Eli. You're interpreting God's word as you see fit. Surely you're not an authorized translator? But that's beside the point. The Lord formed what was yet unformed. No one else helped – we assume."

"We don't assume it. It's a fact. Creation exists, doesn't it? No creation without a Creator. If that isn't proof of His existence – which is what you are aiming at, isn't it? – then what is?"

He paused. "Your questions don't seem to be getting any more sensible. Don't waste my time with silly nonsense."

"As a pious man, you might find it silly, but these questions bother me. Please let me go on." I continued without waiting for an answer. "The Lord created everything there is. That's what I was taught. I wonder how He managed it, though. I'm sure you think that's another silly question, Eli, but it bothers me.

Sorcery? That's too simple. Besides, the Lord considers sorcerers an abomination."[99]

He yawned behind his hand. "We can't understand how He works, Amos. Remember His own words: 'For as the heavens are higher than the earth, so are My ways higher than your ways and My thoughts than your thoughts.'"[100]

"But, Eli, He Himself says something about that creation process: He created with the word. 'God said,' and there it was.[101] I love that image: the creating word, but is that the case? Surely the word doesn't create. It's a medium, a tool. Words can be used to understand wise ideas, but wisdom doesn't create, either. It's not an independent authority. What creates is the spirit, at least the human spirit. The word expresses what the mind has created, as we say. If that applies to the Lord, too, then what the scripture of Genesis should actually have said is, 'The Lord planned everything that was in His mind and He used the word to concretise and manifest His creations.'"

"I can go along with that, Amos, but aren't you playing with words again?"

"No, Eli, I'm not playing. I'm deadly serious. The human mind – that wonderful, abstract product of the continual interaction between reason and imagination – makes man a creative being, at least potentially. That demonstrates that we are, indeed, created in God's image,[102] that we do, indeed, carry a grain of His spirit within us.

To me, that conclusion hits the nail on the head. Firstly, for me it's the convincing proof of God's existence and, secondly, that conclusion has implications. It encapsulates the idea that He commands us to be and remain creative; to be assistant creators; to make every effort to achieve a society that will be better tomorrow than today, in every conceivable way. If that conclusion is correct, then the next implication is that we fall seriously short of the mark."

"My dear boy, you came here, or so you said, to ask questions, but now you're lecturing."

"Don't take it like that, Eli. Sometimes I make statements to provoke discussion and find out whether I'm spouting rubbish."

"That, you're not doing, in any event, but what do you hope to achieve with all this philosophizing? You're seeking the essence of being a Jew. Does this kind of talk get you any further?"

"I think so. I can't see the essence of being a Jew separately from the question of how I should interpret the essence of God and the divine. Anyway, may I continue on the subject for a moment?"

"Please do. I think you're a verbal nit-picker, but your questions do interest me."

I took a deep breath and went on. "Who created the Lord? Did He create Himself? Can anything in the world create itself or does it always require an external force . . . I'm full of questions, Eli . . . And supposing the Lord were created, why didn't the primordial creator create the world himself; why did he need an intermediary? Incidentally, the primordial creator doesn't solve the problem, either, because then who created the primordial creator and so forth? And if there was no primordial creator then where was the Lord before creation? In a world other than ours? Sometimes it makes me dizzy, Eli."

"Me too, Amos. Don't get yourself confused. I haven't got any answers. Man has no answers to the question about the first of all things. I, myself, think that 'the first of all things' is synonymous with the Lord, that He has always been there and that, at some point His spirit moved Him to His acts of creation. Don't bother your head with that kind of question, though. The Lord is the creator of heaven and earth. Be content with that observation. Now go on or go away."

His answer hadn't satisfied me, but Eli seemed annoyed, so I went on to the next question.

B. PREDESTINATION OR SELF-DETERMINATION?

"I will continue, Eli, but I'm very thirsty. Could I have something to drink?" Eli nodded and went off. He came back a while later with a carafe of water in which a couple of slices of lemon were floating. He poured me a glass.

"Continue your interrogation, Amos."

"Who controls my life, Eli, I myself or the Lord?"

"Well, I can give you a clear answer to that question: the Lord. Long before you were born, he decided what your outlook on life would be and to which camp you would belong."[103]

He was reminding me of the strange prophet of doom I'd met in Jerusalem.[104] "What do you mean by camp?"

"There are two. Those inclined to live a righteous life, live according to our Teachings, and the camp of those who have a good chance of ending up on what I will, for want of anything better, call the Lord's blacklist."

"You mean the Lord divides his ultimate creation, mankind, into two categories in advance before they are even brought to life? So He has predetermined our fate?"

"That's the way it is, son. But you will have noticed that I'm expressing myself cautiously. I said 'tendency.' A potentially righteous person can stray from the path. Evil lurks everywhere. The utmost vigilance is always called for. This is why we live isolated from the world. A sinner can always repent, but the way is long and leads inevitably to Qumran."

I was astonished. "But Eli, how did you come by these notions?

The world's not like that. A world consisting of immaculate whites and pitch blacks? Most of us exhibit every shade of grey."

"No, Amos, it's not the Lord who adds those nuances. He is an absolute dualist."[105]

"I don't understand any of this, Eli. Why would He have planned something like that, nipping his own initiative in the bud? It would be flagrantly contradictory to His own words. We were created in His image. He determines; no one determines for Him. The capacity of self-determination is therefore also encapsulated in us."

"You misunderstand me. No one knows what they are pre-destined for. They believe they determine the course of their own life."

"Well, I still don't understand. Why would the Lord have made such a decision? Surely He's interested in whether some-one is willing and able to follow His instructions without inter-vention from above."

"Because He has little confidence in us being able to do so."

"So He made us into puppets?"

"Not puppets, but people who think they possess free will. That makes them feel good. The Lord knows people inside out. After all, He created us."

"So He's pulling the wool over our eyes."

"You could say that; to make our lives happier. That's what He's concerned about."

"I can't believe you're right, Eli. The way I see it, I decide for myself what I do and don't do and the Lord holds me and no one else accountable for my decisions. I decide the course of my ship, not the Lord. I'm the helmsman. I get judged on the grounds of that course. That realization gives my existence both meaning and direction. After all, what gives a life meaning is plotting a course and attempting to reach the destination. I can't accept your way of thinking. Without free will my existence would be bland and therefore pointless. I'd rather not exist. Again, I can't believe that's God's intention. Where did you get such pearls of wisdom? I've never read anything about this in the Holy Scriptures or heard anything about it from my teachers."

"You've been misled, deceived by those so-called teachers of yours. Our Teacher was excluded, even banished. His voice was smothered. You signed your own death warrants." He looked me straight in the eye. "I'll tell you where I get this wisdom."

C. ONE TEACHER OR MANY?

"I didn't pull what you're rightly calling 'wisdom' out of thin air. It was taught to us by the Teacher of Righteousness."[106]

"The Teacher of Righteousness? I've never heard of him, either."

"That doesn't exactly say anything in your favour." Eli's tone was scornful. "Do you know nothing about our background Amos?"

"Virtually nothing, I have to admit."

Eli sat up straight and said, almost ceremoniously, "We are the real Jews with whom the Lord has sealed a new covenant. In other words, we are now the 'true Israel.'"[107]

"But surely, there is only one Israel."

"No, Amos, you're mistaken. Your Israel is the old Israel and the old Israel is finished; it will be destroyed. You've been misled by the priests and the so-called scholars. The Law has been incorrectly interpreted; the Temple ritual has become a caricature of what it should be. High Priests have even called themselves king and neglected their priestly duties. Lots of priests are corrupt. For them, money prevails above spirit. Do you protest? No, you allow it to go on. Later, or actually very soon, that will count very heavily against you. Mark my words. The end is near. Our group has found the right way."[108]

"Only the Qumran community?"

"No, the group of Essenes."

"So who was your guide?"

"For the umpteenth time: the Teacher of Righteousness,"

replied Eli, irritated. "He was a priest – a real priest; a descendant of Zadok[109] – one whom the Lord endowed with gifts. He revealed to him the true meaning of the Holy Scriptures and the prophets' sayings. He was closer to the Lord than the prophets, with the possible exception of Moses.[110] He didn't have a good word to say about the Kings and High Priests of the House of Hasmon."[111]

"Should I see him as a kind of second Moses?"

"A Super Moses, I should say. Like Moses, he communicated directly with the Lord and not only through visions and dreams.[112] He was chosen. The interpretation our Teacher gave of the Holy Scriptures is the definitive interpretation. That's the one we have to adhere to."

"Is 'Jerusalem' really finished as far as you're concerned?"

"Over and done with!"

"Do you still really feel like Jews, or are you paving the way for a new religion?"

"We feel eminently Jewish; as I said, the 'new Israel,' the 'true Israel.' Not a new religion, but the pearl in the shell of the old religion. That pearl will last forever. There, in that pearl, is where we, the Children of the Light, abide. The Children of Darkness abide in the shell and that shell shall perish horribly."[113]

"But Eli, this way you're creating a division amongst our people. There can only be one chosen people, I assume."

"Quite right, young man, one of them is finished. Haven't you understood that yet?"

"I have understood, but I find the idea too horrific to be true and your judgement of 'Jerusalem' far too pessimistic. Plenty of things have, indeed, gone wrong over the past few years, but there are men of goodwill there, too. They constitute the majority. They're attempting to salvage what they can of the situation. You claim that your Teacher is wiser than ours, but I'm not convinced."

"But, Amos, he was instructed by the Lord himself. Doesn't that say enough?"

"That's what our sages say, as well. They teach us that Moses was instructed by the Lord on Mount Sinai in two ways. He received commandments, which were written down, and he received oral explanation of those commandments. That has been handed down to our current teachers through the prophets and many generations of wise men. They discuss the 'Oral Torah' year in, year out. The Lord encourages them to do so. 'My words are no longer in heaven,' He said.[114] All words devoted to this are God's words.[115] None of the debaters has the last word. In questions regarding the Teachings, a consensus is reached or a majority decision is taken."

"Drivel, boy. Those aren't the Lord's words; they're the words of your so-called teachers themselves. Only our Teacher has, himself, communicated with the Lord, but enough of this, Amos. We follow one teacher. Only his voice is authoritative and that's the end of it."

D. THE HOME STRETCH?

"I wonder whether you really understand what's at stake: heaven or hell, I mean that literally. A small kernel of our people will survive and, ultimately, gain everlasting life. The vast majority is heading to its doom. They'll be destroyed and reach their final destination in hell. The end time is near, young man. Have you never heard of that?"[116]

"Not really. Priests treat it as a nasty folk story. In the school I went to, they were critical of it."

Eli banged his fist on the table. "They don't want to hear the truth. They're scared of it. The world as it is now will soon come to an end, probably even in your time. The final battle that proceeds it will be horrific and blood-drenched. Finally, the righteous, the Children of Light, will extinguish the power of darkness for good. Time will cease to exist and become eternity. Everlasting happiness awaits the righteous, everlasting misery the obstinate."

"I'm familiar with that doom scenario, Eli, but to be honest I don't believe in it. Time will never cease to exist. Time flows; it never stands still. There will always be time. Time that lies behind us, time that is now and time still to come."

"You're talking about this world, Amos. In the next, in the *Olam Haba* (Hebrew), that no longer applies. Time disappears. Nothing happens any longer, and past, present and future are time categories linked to events. Time, the perception of time, evaporates. It'll be replaced by the perception of bliss or despair, which will exist permanently."

"If you're right, Eli, I'm certainly not looking forward to such a land of milk, honey and happiness. It sounds like interminable boredom. I need events. I'm very aware of the present, but I look forward, I want to build a future, to my own plan, with my past included in that plan. Without time, without any perception of time, I can't imagine life, any life that would be worth living."

"You don't know what you're saying, Amos. Happiness doesn't get boring. Happiness evokes longing for more, almost insatiably. You'll receive that 'more.' The feeling of happiness multiplies until, finally, you reach a state of the sublime, the perfect."

"The sublime what . . ." my voice faltered, "So what does that mean: the perfect?"

"The divine, young man, that is sublime and perfect. I can't say more than that. Merging with the divine, that's the ultimate experience of happiness. It takes you back to your beginnings. To put it simply: back home."

"All that's a bit too grandiloquent for me. It goes right over my head. I thought that what mattered was what we achieve here on Earth. Our task is to make something better of this world. If we succeed, I see that as a form of happiness. Swooning over boundless heavenly bliss doesn't add anything."

"One doesn't exclude the other. Here on Earth, we endeavour to live life entirely righteously."

"You're kidding yourself, Eli. You live the life you do in the expectation of a heavenly reward. You lead a life centred strictly on yourself. You do little or nothing for your fellow man. You don't bear witness to your views, you don't even try to set people on your path, warn them of the disaster you believe is imminent. Am I supposed to admire that?"

Eli shoved his chair back noisily. "My patience is beginning to wear thin. You don't want to listen and you don't want to learn. You attack without any knowledge of what you're talking about. Now I'm going to have something to eat."

"Can I come with you?

"No, you're not welcome in the dining room. Go to the kitchen if you're hungry."

"Are you coming back?"

"I'll see. Wait here."

And without another word he left the room.

In the kitchen was a relatively-young-looking man. "You must be Amos. Eli just warned me you'd be coming." He gave me a haughty look and handed me a piece of bread and a glass of water. "And now I'll have to ask you to leave. You're not welcome here."

Well, that couldn't have been much blunter, I thought. I said, "You're very hospitable." He turned on his heel and walked away. I went back to the reception room and waited for what seemed like hours. Finally, Eli came back. "We're on totally different tracks, Amos. But I've come back, nonetheless. You're showing interest in our community. I appreciate that and, unless I'm mistaken, you haven't finished asking questions."

"Not by a long chalk, Eli."

I hesitated for a moment.

"Don't be shy, Amos, ask whatever you like," he said, continuing rather scornfully with, "My convictions are quite firm."

"If I understand you correctly, Eli, you foresee a world of unending happiness for a particular, privileged group."

"That's right, a small group. Our Teacher spoke of the 'Children of the Light.'"

"I assume that, by that, you mean the Essenes."

"You assume rightly."

"So you can look forward to the end time with confidence."

"Oh no, you've got that wrong."

"But, surely, your position was predestined?"

"Yes, but, as I said, it's conditional. We have to realize that destiny here on earth. You can still fall by the wayside and ruin your chances for good. A worldly life is full of temptations. That's why the Essenes retreat from the world. Here, in Qumran, we go the furthest in that respect. We've renounced our wives and families. You won't find any women here. Qumran is a male society. Sexual intercourse is taboo here."

"What on earth do you expect to achieve with that?"

"Concentration."

"Concentration on what?"

"On the approaching end time."

"What you're doing defeats the object, in my view. Desire, longing, they can't be suppressed. Attempts to do so just increase their intensity."

"We do our best, Amos, and if ever we fail we cleanse ourselves from such moral contamination."

Evidently, I looked disbelieving. "You don't understand this, I see. I'll explain once more, but then we'll let the subject drop.

We've renounced all our possessions. We live in a community of goods, so none of us knows grinding poverty and none excessive luxury.[117] We live extremely simply. We work the land, providing for our own needs and, when we're not working, we study the Holy Scriptures. In short, we have a sober life and avoid pleasure."

"I can't understand such an attitude to life, Eli. The Lord invited us to enjoy all the good things we received from Him. We're called upon to multiply. That inevitably generates pleasure. Our neighbors merit our attention, particularly the deprived. So should we be allowed to abandon our women and children? It's an outrage! Certainly, we're part of a community, but we're also individuals with the right to a private life. As far as I know, Moses never praised the commune as the ideal form of society."[118]

"Evidently you still don't realize you're at a turning point. It's sink or swim. Pleasure demands more, leading to self-indulgence. We have to keep our spiritual house in order. At all costs. Your fate only becomes sealed once the forces of darkness have finally been defeated. Only then will it become clear who is on the right side of the divide."

"I can't imagine that the Lord recognizes the divide you're referring to. He knows man like the back of his hand, as they say. I'm convinced He differentiates. Anyway, I understand you can lose your status as a chosen one. Can an outsider still attain that status here on Earth?"

"Yes, in principle, but it's a long, hard route. You have to be accepted as a novice here in Qumran, devote years to studying, strictly observe our house rules and not be found wanting when you are finally weighed by our elders."[119]

"And what if you are?"

"Then you have to leave our community. We don't accept any unripe apples in our basket."[120]

"That's rather a hard, intransigent attitude, Eli. Surely, your role model, the Lord, is 'loving and merciful.'"[121]

"The Lord isn't our role model. He is entirely inimitable in His perfection. Our role model is our Teacher and he demanded iron discipline."

"Everything you're telling me sounds rather disturbing, Eli. What happens to the Jews who you feel have fallen out of favour with the Lord?"

"They're lost for good. What exactly happens to them is unclear. They probably disappear forever into the *Sheol* (Hebrew), the underworld. And a good thing, too; they're in Satan's power."

"What will happen to the heathens?"

"I don't know. Our Teacher never talked about them. I assume there's still some hope for them. After all, they've had no chance to know the true teachings. I give them the benefit of the doubt."

"So the only hope for the survival of our people lies here in Qumran. That's what I deduce from what you're saying."

"That's exactly right."

"But then our future looks extremely bleak. Your community consists entirely of men. Unless the end time is about to dawn, then you'll die out here and our people will be wiped prematurely from history."

"Now, there you're wrong, Amos. There's another group of Essenes, too. They've continued living in the towns and villages. They keep themselves apart from the other inhabitants, but they stay with their families, retain their possessions and continue their work. They adhere less strictly to the doctrine than we do, but they keep to our rules as far as they can and we recruit the new generation from them.

I went over to the window and looked out for a while.

"You're evidently upset by my words, Amos, but please sit back down." I did as he said.

"You're undoubtedly sincere, Eli, but please allow me to be candid, as well. I don't hear any respect for your fellow man in your words. You drop your neighbors like a hot brick, you disparage them, devalue them. Isn't that contrary to one of the basic commandments of the only universal Teacher, the Lord?"[122]

"I see you've been listening attentively. I only respect those who respect His representative, the Teacher of Righteousness. The others have strayed from God's path. Showing respect for them would mean collaborating with Satan, betraying the Lord."

"In my view, there are several ways that lead to the Lord, Eli. I find your view hard, intransigent and, if I may say so, ungodly."

"Hard, but realistic and pleasing to God. Serving the Lord is a question of all or nothing. You can't do deals with Him. You follow His rules or you end up on a slippery slope and slide off, irrevocably. Fidelity can't be diluted. Diluted fidelity is infidelity."

I sighed. "We'll never be able to convince one another. I don't respect your views and you don't respect mine. We aren't even able to honor God's commandment from that point of view. I'd better just drop the subject."

"As you wish."

"May I address another point?"

"Go ahead." I'm curious."

E. THE PLACE OF DEATH, OR *THE PLACE*?[123]

"Your community has settled in a desolate desert at the edge of a lake in which nothing lives, nothing grows. A place where death seems to reign. A place that our God, the God of life, has seemingly forsaken."

"You've got it all wrong, Amos. This is no godforsaken place; here, with us, is His domicile."

"Again, a statement that's entirely alien to me, Eli. The Lord doesn't dwell here. He wouldn't feel at home. Our Temple in Jerusalem is His permanent residence, whatever the priesthood might get up to. I'm fully convinced of that."

Eli remained apparently calm. "Not any longer, young man, not any longer. To put it crudely: the Lord has moved house. Make no mistake, the current Jerusalem will be destroyed during the final battle, including the Temple. City and Temple will rise again, more radiant than ever."[124]

"Rebuilt by you, no doubt."

"That's right."

"And where will that New Jerusalem arise?"

"In the *Olam Haba*."

"And where do you think that 'coming world' will be located?"

"That hasn't been revealed yet. It could be here on Earth."

"On Earth?" I interrupted, "A Kingdom of God on Earth? Surely that's a dream; this Earth doesn't lend itself to that, at all!"

"Let me finish, Amos; your insolence borders on the intolerable, even for a seasoned teacher. Anyway, a second possibility is that the 'coming world' will arise in heavenly spheres and that's something we have no way of imagining. You remember how the Lord replied to Moses by the burning bush, when he asked His name: [125]"I am who I am." The Lord decides as he wishes. Man can't predict. We have to wait and see what he decides."

"So even the Children of the Light haven't been told."

"Sarcasm doesn't suit you, young man. I'll put it down to youthful arrogance and pay it no heed.

You noticed that our surroundings are literally dead. Indeed, this place was not chosen at random. In our philosophy, death is central. We, too, will die. That could be a natural death or we could perish in the final battle. Only then will we find out if we have proved ourselves to be true 'Children of the Light,' whether we qualify for everlasting happiness. As I already said, it can all go wrong at the last moment."

"Then fear must reign here in Qumran."

"We are uncertain, young man, and where uncertainty dominates, fear dominates."

"How can you stand that: living in fearful expectation until death comes?"

"Until that time comes, fear does keep a tight rein on us."

"So the 'cost' comes before the 'benefit," you might say."

Eli's face hardened. "Another cheeky remark. You trivialize our outlook on life. I find that extremely annoying. I'm not prepared to continue the discussion like this."

"Please excuse me, Master, I expressed myself clumsily. I'm only trying to understand."

"All right then, but this is the last time. Your thirst for answers is insatiable and I'm not sure about your tactics. You ask a question, receive an answer, then comment in the form of a question, eliciting yet another answer. And so on. You're making me tired. That's enough for today. Let's both go and get some sleep and you can come back in the morning, always assuming you haven't had enough yet."

"As you said, I'm insatiable. I'll be there."

Eli left, shaking his head.

F. FEAR OF CONTAMINATION

Eli made me wait into the early afternoon. I used the time to look around the settlement.

Eli sat down, without greeting me, and started in immediately. "This time, I'll begin. Don't think that all we're doing here is passively sitting around waiting. We work on the land, study the Holy Scriptures."

"You don't have to convince me of that, Eli, I've seen it for myself. Believe me, I'm really interested in the way you think. I'm trying to understand you and, when I don't, I express criticism. I can't help it."

"We're not so used to criticism from our pupils here. They listen, absorb and accept."

"I can't accept what I can't understand, Eli, but never mind, I want to avoid getting into dispute. I've got a question that's simply informative, I believe. This morning, I saw a lot of men bathing, submerging themselves entirely. Why was that?"

"For us, Amos, cleanliness is an essential daily concern."

"Why is that, Eli? Do you want to appear before the Lord with a fresh face and clean hands if you die unexpectedly?"

I was shocked at my own choice of words. Weigh them before you speak, I thought, but Eli appeared to take it amiably.

"Not with a clean face, Amos, but with a cleansed spirit, a fresh conscience."

"Again, I don't understand you. You leave the Temple in Jerusalem behind, but you still see purity as crucial. Surely purity relates specifically to Temple services? That's what I was taught. You come into the presence of God's spirit in the Temple. God Himself, in other words, as He is pure spirit and has no corporeality. He is the God of life and the living. That is His greatest creation. The Lord mustn't be confronted with the opposite of life. Any contact with death or with the dying, makes you ritually unclean."

Eli interrupted me. "Stop, I'm not an infant. You still don't understand the significance of Qumran. Here is where God's Spirit dwells. Our community has become the Temple. So, for us, purity is a permanent rather than an occasional concern. Being ritually and morally cleansed is therefore essential."

"Morally cleansed, you say?" I was amazed. "You can't wash sins away."

"Oh yes, you can, son. We feel misbehavior and bad thoughts sully not only the mind but also the body."

"So you can wash away injustices you have committed on others with water? Is that not insincere, in fact false symbolism? Self-serving symbolism? Symbolism that provides an easy way to salve your conscience? The Lord can't be fooled you know!"

I felt myself becoming furious. Watch your words, Amos, I thought, your tone of voice risks becoming provocative again. Eli remained calm.

"It's not an easy way. It's the last step in a process. It has to be preceded by confessing and showing remorse. Cleansing is the last step."

"No, Eli, the last but one. The last is a change of mentality, showing compassion and willingness to compensate any you may have wronged."

Eli nodded with what seemed a fatherly look.

"You put it very well, Amos, and I agree with you. Compassion is, indeed, a high priority for us. We help where help is needed. Here in Qumran and when we are out and about. Those needing help will never call on us in vain."[126]

"Without exception? Does that also apply to those you consider to be 'Children of Darkness'"?

"No; they're the devil's accomplices. We're not collaborators."

"Good and bad. Real people, people of flesh and blood, with their strong and their weak sides, they don't exist in your eyes. But there are so few saints and outright villains."

"Wrong again, Amos. Saints are, indeed, very rare. But those who strive for sanctity are more numerous."

"No doubt they are based here."

"Yes, they are, son. There are many evil individuals, though. Those who disregard the will of the Lord. Why else would a hell have been created?"

"Are you sure it exists?"

"As sure as I sit here."

"And what if the soul were not immortal and the dead were never to arise again?"

"That would be a sign that the Lord has left our world. Then my world image would be in tatters. Then I would rather die on the spot."

"You have a great deal of certainty, Eli. I don't. I have doubts. So do I envy you? No. On one hand, I seek certainty. On the other hand, though, I do like doubt. It keeps my mind in motion and sets me to thinking."

"You elevate doubt to a kind of cult, Amos. You seem to take delight in it. Aren't you rather playing the role of the ambitious intellectual?"

"No, Eli, I'm not playing a role. I'm playing myself."

An uncomfortable silence fell. I went over to the window and stared out at the barren desert landscape. I like the man, I thought. One massive block of principles. But what a distance there is between us. Can we both really call ourselves Jews?"

"Amos, my boy," I heard Eli call. "Do you want to stop?"

"No, I don't, Eli, but I would like to take a little break. I was suddenly overcome with an unpleasant feeling."

"Out with it, then."

"Well, when I was walking around here this morning, I got the impression people were avoiding me. When I went past the dining room, the door was slammed in my face before I'd even asked for anything. In the kitchen, I was given a chunk of bread. Hardly a word was addressed to me. It was as if they saw an enemy in me. I'm not used to that from fellow Jews. Am I unclean?"

"Now, that's where the problem lies. You're a stranger from Jerusalem and not recognized as one of our novices. They don't know if you're an Essene. You could be a heathen – and we don't like to mix with them – or a fallen Jew, one 'who follows the way of darkness, led by the Angel of Darkness.'[127] Then, for us, you are, indeed, impure. The people avoid contact because they don't want to be contaminated. Even if a junior member of our community touches a senior, that senior has to go and bathe to cleanse himself.[128] So eating together with us is out of the question."

"That's pretty condescending, Eli."

"The truth can be hard, Amos. Besides, for us the meal is about far more than satisfying your hunger. It's a sacred event. Even novices aren't allowed to participate. We cleanse ourselves beforehand, then dress in robes of white, the color of purity."[129]

"But isn't the wearing of white robes reserved for priests conducting Temple services?"

"You really are stubborn. Our community is the Temple now and our members the new priests. Get that into your head. The bread and wine are first blessed and then, while we eat, hardly a word is spoken.[130] That way, a connection is made between the Lord and our community and we interpret God's call to: 'Be holy because I, the Lord your God, am holy.'"[131]

"You exclude people, even your prospective kindred spirits. I don't think that's what the Lord means by holy. You don't want anything to do with the others. That's what I call profane behavior. Of the bad variety. Still, who am I to make such a claim?"

"Indeed, who are you? A beginner with the tendency to overrate himself!"

"Aren't you taking a big risk, Eli?"

"What do you mean?"

"For hours now you've been talking with an impure beginner. Doesn't that make you unclean?"

"Thank you for your concern, Amos, but I'm permitted to do it. I'm a teacher here, taking a beginner under my wing. Rest assured, though, I go and cleanse myself thoroughly after every discussion with you."

"Excuse me, Eli, but I find your words appalling. You talk as if I were contaminated with *tzaraäth*."[132]

"Exactly, and so you are, spiritually. You are under the spell of the 'Prince of Darkness.' He has a penchant for followers. You could drag others down with you into misfortune."

"Really, Eli? Me, that beginner? Yes, I'm groping around in obscurity, trying to find myself. But I've never come across that dark prince you're talking about. In my own way, I attempt to do the right thing, even though I'm also a beginner in that respect."

"Good deeds aren't enough, son. Your whole existence, everything you do must be modelled on God's guidelines. You're not on the right track. That begins here, in Qumran."

I felt my irritation growing. "I'm beginning to wonder whether you, here in Qumran, might be on the wrong track. You suffer from pride. It's not I, but you who will fall.[133] I don't need you people. If I were on the wrong track, then I would turn directly to the Lord. I'm sure you know what a *baal teshuva* is.[134] If I'm sincere then He will accept me.

I experience the Lord as a Being who supports, understands, punishes where necessary, but also forgives. You've transformed Him into an irreconcilable, intolerant authority. Is that what the Teacher of Righteousness taught you? If so, then he's the one who is mistaken, not I."

Eli went to the door and opened it. "I've had more than enough of this. You insult our Teacher and humiliate God's chosen people. I ought to throw you out, but I'm not going to. Why not? Because I have compassion for the misled and we, here in Qumran, can help someone like that repent."

"You're not sending me away?"

"No, you can come back tomorrow as long as you moderate your tone."

"I'll try to. Have a good evening."

Without another word, Eli walked away.

G. PROPHECY OR DREAM?

I was nervous when I met Eli again the following day. Shocked as I was by his words, evidently I, in turn, had deeply insulted him. I need not have worried, though. He even smiled as I came in.

"Sit down, I'm sure you slept well." It sounded ironic and was obviously meant to.

"I certainly didn't, Eli. I was ashamed of my behavior yesterday. Not of the content of my words, but of the tone. I'd like to apologize."

"Fine, fine. I accept your apology, but you certainly are a stubborn, hard-headed person. Now, what else can I help you with?"

"You base your existence here on the sayings of the Teacher of Righteousness. Like Moses, he is said to have been instructed directly by the Lord."

"That's right, son."

"The Lord presented himself to your Teacher alone, not to the entire people, and he put nothing down in writing. The comparison with Moses doesn't ring true. That gives me doubts."

"The Lords decides His own course. Our Leader did that, too. You weren't involved, young man."

"Could you tell me something about the Teacher's message?"

"Not in just a few words. You'd have to become a novice here for that. Let me make one important point, though. The Lord wanted to clean up His words, brush off the dust and dirt that have covered them over the course of time, partly through the fault of your so-called scholars. He entrusted that task to our Teacher."

"He interpreted God's words."

"Exactly."

"But that's just what our teachers are trying to do, as well.

And that's how – to put it rather crudely – you get as many interpretations as interpreters."

"That might apply to your interpreters, the Pharisees. Our Teacher received one interpretation. That's something different. That interpretation is binding. Our entire people should have accepted that reading. They refused and so signed their own death warrant."

"How can you be so sure of that?"

"You only have to read prophets such as Isaiah and Jeremiah. The Lord complains about the people of Israel, 'the sinful nation,' that has forsaken the Lord.[135] Jeremiah predicts what will happen:[136]

> 'I will bring on them a disaster they cannot escape. Although they cry out to me, I will not listen to them.'"

"When it really comes to a crunch, though, He always helps us up again, Eli."

"Not this time, my boy. It's over for you; His patience has run out. It's been predicted:[137]

> 'Behold, days are coming,' declares the Lord, 'when I will make a new covenant with the house of Israel and with the house of Judah, not like the covenant which I made with their fathers in the day I took them by the hand to bring them out of the land of Egypt, My covenant which they broke, although I was a husband to them.'
>
> 'But this is the covenant which I will make with the house of Israel after those days,' declares the Lord, 'I will put My law within them and on their heart I will write it.'"

"How do you know that you will come out of it unscathed?"

"It's all set down in the Holy Scriptures and our Teacher has opened our eyes. I'll give you an example. Remember the prophet Ezekiel's vision? He saw a valley full of bones that were very dry, but the Lord brought them back to life.[138]

We were taught that this prediction concerned our entire people. Ezekiel prophesied during our exile in Babylon. They say this is how the prophet gave the people hope that everything would turn out well in the end. Wrong! Our Teacher learned the correct interpretation of the vision. It refers to the end time. Resurrection only applies to those Israelites who 'love His name.' Only they will be rewarded for their fidelity."[139]

I didn't let him finish. "So those statements refer to your community. That's what the Teacher told you."

"You have an envisioning mind, young man."

I ignored his snide remark. "Let me remind you, Eli, that the same Ezekiel heard from the Lord that he will take the Israelites from the nations, gather them from all the lands and bring them into their own land.[140] He doesn't talk of a permanent split."

"You know your Ezekiel. That does you credit, but the Lord does make that distinction:[141]

> Yet you say, 'The way of the Lord is not just.' Hear, you Israelites: Is my way unjust? Is it not your ways that are unjust? If a righteous person turns from their righteousness and commits sin, they will die for it; because of the sin they have committed they will die.

I can see you still don't believe me. I'll give you another example of a prophecy that refers to our group.

The prophet Isaiah talks of a voice that will call out in the wilderness. The voice of the 'bringer of joy,' calls to 'prepare the way for the Lord; make straight in the desert a highway for our God.'[142] It's we who are preparing the way.[143] If that doesn't tell you enough, then I've nothing more to say."

"No, it's not enough for me, Eli. Who is to say those words refer to you? These are retrospective claims, not prophecies.

Anyone can say that specific texts from the Holy Scriptures refer to them or their group."

Eli's right foot began to twitch. "My claims come from the mouth of our Teacher, the highest authority ever on earth; higher even than Moses."[144]

"That's your opinion. Our teachers have never mentioned him. Surely, you're not going to claim that he was the Messiah, God's representative? He died and since then things have only gotten worse. Incidentally, I've never heard of a Messiah dying before he has even begun his work."

Eli reddened. "I've never claimed that our Teacher was the Messiah. I am, however, convinced he will return."

I continued without pause. Looking back, it must have seemed like provocation. "Did that Teacher really speak on behalf of the Lord? Isn't it possible that it's not we – those to whom you refer as the 'fallen Jews' – but *you* who have turned your back on the Lord? Isn't it rather significant that this Teacher of yours wasn't presented to our people by the Lord himself? That would have been the obvious thing to do if he really had been His representative."

Eli scraped his chair back and stood up. "Enough is enough. We speak different languages. For a moment, I'd hoped to be able to convince you that your only hope lay here in Qumran. That hope has proven vain."

"I'm sorry to have disappointed you, Eli, but your image of our world is too hopeless for me. You see mankind as cast upon the earth, his fate already largely sealed in advance, struggling to survive morally here in anxious expectation of what the end time will bring. That kills any initiative to fight for a better society here on earth. In your world, there is no longer any messianic fire. The only light you see shining is in the *Olam Haba* and then that's only for a small group of individuals favoured by the Lord. Privileged without any comprehensible reason, as far as I can see.

I find such a world . . . sorry, world image, discouraging. I can't imagine it was God who cooked it up. Your Judaism is not the Judaism I'm looking for."

Eli shook his head and walked out of the room. When he reached the door, he turned. "Wait there a moment." He came back with a bag. "I've brought you something to eat and drink. And now go. Farewell, although I doubt that will be the case."

He walked off: an old man with a stoop. I felt as much regret as satisfaction from my outbursts.

H. REFLECTION

Back in the burning sun, I set out once more for Jerusalem. Have I learnt much here? I wondered. Undoubtedly. Was I the wiser for it? No. I found the spiritual climate in Qumran oppressive. Repellent, even. How dare they doctor our Teachings like that? What an egocentric community. All they're bothered about is saving their own souls. The Lord preserve me from even the slightest sin in deed or thought – that's their motto. What a narrow-minded atmosphere! Anxiously waiting to see what's in store for them after death. Wanting nothing to do with joy. They're focused on death, not life. The Lord is seen no longer as a beacon of hope but as a source of suffocating fear. Predestination has taken the place of self-determination. They feel helpless, pre-programmed, but at the same time a member of a select company of God's protégés. What a bizarre combination of humility and inflated egotism. Self-aggrandizement underpinned with the assertion that texts appropriated from the Holy Scriptures refer to their community. And these are supposed to have been entrusted to them by some mysterious Teacher of Righteousness, on behalf of the Lord. With such a postulate, you can always justify the unjustifiable.

I didn't see any trace of empathy in Qumran. Anyone who isn't part of their group is, literally, condemned, deemed morally impure. Such disregard for their fellow man!

I wonder if one who has no mercy toward another like himself, can seek pardon for his own sins?[145] The Lord doesn't tolerate arrogance.[146] Will the judgement of the heavenly court – if it ever comes to that – not be the exact opposite of what the Qumran community is counting on?

And how simplistic their view of humanity is! Dividing it mercilessly into two – the good and the bad. For the good, an everlasting feast awaits, for the bad only everlasting destruction. I can't imagine that the Lord is such a black-and-white thinker. He knows mankind too well for that.

A grey film hangs over life in Qumran. You're no longer allowed to enjoy anything: not your family, not the union of man and wife, not the fruits of your labor. I thought we were told to 'choose life,'[147]– this life – not some, as far as I'm concerned, speculative life in the future.

I'm very much afraid that there, in Qumran, they've sketched the outlines of a new religion, without having received any convincing divine mandate to do so. In my eyes, that borders on blasphemy. Perhaps that goes too far, but what I experienced in Qumran was the opposite of the Jewishness I seek, which, as yet, I see only dimly in my mind's eye. I left Qumran behind me, literally and figuratively.

Fig. 7 The Wadi Kerit where the prophet Elijah hid and, thanks to the Lord, was fed by the raven (1 Kings 17:2–4).
From: Ben Gurion, D. (Ed) (1974). *The Jews in their land*, London: Aldus Books.

Elijah did not die, but was taken up to heaven. The prophet Malachi predicted that Elijah would return (Malachi 3:23). John's followers believed they saw in him the return of Elijah, heralding the Messiah.

CHAPTER 6

YOCHANAN (ALIAS JOHN), THE "BAPTIST"

False securities lack persuasiveness. Certainty of belief is a contradiction in terms, a form of self-deception.

For the hope of the Godly is like dust that is blown away with the wind; like a thin froth that is driven away with the storm; like as the smoke which is dispersed here and there with a tempest, and passeth away as the remembrance of a guest that tarrieth but a day. But the righteous live for evermore; their reward also is with the Lord, and the care of them is with the most High.

Wisdom of Solomon 5:14–15

A. BEYOND CERTAINTY

I walked north along the bank of the River Jordan only at night, to avoid the midday heat. My water supply was running short. I had to find a settlement.

I'd heard from my father that there was a man roving these parts who had gained a big following. Many of his followers believed him to be the Messiah.[148] He was calling on people to repent and be baptized.[149] I understood the appeal, or at least the first part of it. It was heard regularly in our land, but I didn't understand what he meant by baptism.

I had more questions. Why was he speaking in the wilderness and not in synagogues? Why were so many people leaving hearth and home to follow him in this barren wasteland? Did he, himself, also believe he was the Messiah? If so, how had he come by that information? I wanted to speak to the man. I was sure that he had more to say than just that the end time was approaching. I was in his territory now and hoping to chance upon him.

I was in luck. I suddenly heard a clamour in the distance. It sounded like cheering. I followed the sound and saw, some way off, a big group of people slowly coming my way. At the front walked an imposing figure. Tall, heavily built, with a thick mass of black, curly hair.

From that distance, he seemed covered in hair, as the prophet Elijah was said to have been,[150] but as he approached I could see it was an optical illusion. His "clothes were woven from coarse camel hair."[151] If this really is Yochanan, I said to myself, then I can imagine people mistaking him for Elijah, the prophet whom the Lord is said to have taken "up to heaven in a whirlwind," while he wasn't yet dead[152] and is predicted to return to earth one day as a herald for the Messiah.[153]

When I caught up with the group, I spoke to its leader. It turned out that he was, indeed, Yochanan.

"I'd like to speak to you, sir!"

"Not now, friend. It's not convenient. Join the group." His voice was commanding and I could hardly do otherwise than obey.

At one point, Yochanan stopped. He turned and spoke, or rather bellowed, to his followers, "Repent, for the kingdom of heaven has come near,[154] believe the good news."[155] He added the words that had so intrigued me: "Have yourself baptized." The motive, in my eyes, was even stranger, though: have yourself baptized "to receive forgiveness of your sins."[156]

The man next to me nudged me. "You've only just arrived, young man, but do you realize who you're looking at? This is the man the prophet Isaiah spoke of when he said we would hear a voice calling, "In the wilderness prepare the way for the Lord; make straight in the desert a highway for our God."[157]

I pretended I hadn't heard it before.[158] "That's quite some claim, friend. Is he the Messiah? The man who will redeem us from Roman tyranny and found another society, led by priests? I can't imagine. He looks more like a lone wolf rebel, a reborn Samson, than a disciplined military leader. Besides, he doesn't have an army."

"Now there you're wrong, my friend: Yochanan isn't the Messiah himself, he's his Herald. What's more, the Messiah won't found a kingdom on earth, he'll found it in heaven, under the auspices of not priests, but the Lord Himself."

I reacted as if this idea were new to me, too.[159] "What do you mean? Such a kingdom is impossible. Heaven is the private domain of the Lord. No other being can survive there. Heaven and Earth are irreconcilable. The Lord is a concept that exceeds human comprehension. That applies to His domain, too. The Lord himself told Moses as much when Moses asked to see Him. His reply was, 'You cannot see My face, for no man can see Me and live!'[160] Moses was the only person in the world to see His back, as a vague echo of His being. A kingdom in heaven accessible to mankind is impossible."

"That's an age-old misconception, my friend. Something the priests have convinced you of. When you die, your soul leaves. The soul is a temporary component of us, a breath of the Lord.[161] That can never be lost. It returns to its origin, to heaven."

"You say the soul is a breath of the Lord, neighbor. That may be so, but that breath colors our whole existence – our spiritual existence, as well as our physical existence. A body without a soul is a dead body and without a body the soul can't exist."

"Quite right, but in due course the body will be resurrected, too, reunited with the soul, and will then have to appear before a heavenly court. That's what Yochanan maintains: a final judgement is hanging over our heads."

It's like being in Qumran again, I thought. The same

preoccupation with death and what happens thereafter. "How can you still have any pleasure in life with such frightening ideas?" I asked.

He shrugged. "My pleasure in this worldly life has, indeed, evaporated, but Yochanan has given me the assurance that everything will be all right in the end."

"Good for you, neighbor, but let me come back to the issue of the soul. I can't imagine the soul can exist alone, even temporarily. I mean, you can't separate the color of a flower from the flower itself."

"Think about it for a moment, my friend. The soul contains something from the Lord himself, as I said: a breath. He surely wouldn't let such a precious commodity rot away. Otherwise, at some point, he would be burnt out or, to put it a better way, short of breath. And if you doubt that the Lord can bring the dead back to life, then remember that He who created mankind also has the power to recreate someone."

I didn't pursue the subject. After all, I thought to myself, you're not going to change the minds of impassioned people. Qumran had already taught me that much.

"Never mind," I said, "You're not going to convince me. I refuse to mix the profane with the sacred. Man is as he is. A fallible creature; well-meaning, but brimming with shortcomings. God is God, a unique being, a manifestation of the superhuman, a being without shortcomings, whom I trust unconditionally. I can't enter His domain, I wouldn't want to. So dead means irrevocably dead."

"Are you entirely sure of that, young man? Don't you see any future beyond death?"

"No, I don't. Am I certain there isn't any? No, I used to be certain, but now I have my doubts. Against my better judgement, though, I do cherish some hope. Hope that something of me will survive. At least a memory, probably what you call my soul. I don't like the idea of the death struggle being the finale. Your certainty is my hope."

"That's cold comfort, boy. Vague hope of a vague, uncertain future."

"I'll just have to make do with that, neighbor, but that comfort is not as cold as you think. Our existence offers possibilities, rather than certainties. It's actually certainties that impoverish life and possibilities that enrich it. Possibilities are the spice of life. They encourage us to choose a destination and attempt to reach it. That gives life a sense of purpose."

My neighbor shrugged his shoulders. "There's no bridging the gap between our views," he said, scornfully.

"I agree with you on that."

The man to my right nudged me. "I couldn't help hearing your conversation. You were doubting what he said; but he didn't make it up. This is what Yochanan tells us day in, day out."

"On whose authority does the man speak? Is he a priest or a scribe?"

"He's a man with an impeccable pedigree. His father, Zechariah, was a priest; his mother, Elizabeth, is a descendant of Aaron.[162] So he does speak with some authority."

"That's as may be, but he speaks with such self-assurance, as if he has no doubts, no uncertainties; as if he can read God's thoughts. I encountered the same attitude in Qumran. I don't like it much. Does Yochanan know that community?"

"I believe he's had some contact with them. Hush, though: Yochanan's going to speak again."

Yochanan had climbed up onto a stone. He had a heavy, sonorous voice and emphasized his words with broad arm gestures. "Repent," he said again, repeating the command several times, each time more loudly than before. "The end time is near. Repent, repent your sins, live a virtuous life and be righteous towards one another."[163] His voice took on an ominous tone. "The axe is already at the root of the trees, and every tree that does not produce good fruit will be cut down and thrown into the fire."[164]

Again, that awful moral exclusivity, it occurred to me. A paradisiacal society beckons, but only for the immaculately pure of spirit. Is there not a world of possibilities between undiluted virtue and unadulterated vice? Wouldn't the Lord know about it?

A group of spectators at the front began muttering. Four priests and a few men who I assumed were legal scholars. Yochanan stopped talking for a moment. The priests shouted, "You're terrifying people with your unhealthy ideas. Who do you think you are?"

Yochanan raised his finger and retorted angrily, "You brood of vipers, who warned you to flee from the wrath to come? Do not suppose that you can say to yourselves, 'We will be secure. We have Abraham for our father.'"[165]

I don't think you've understood the Sinai Covenant, I said to myself. There is no automatic safety for the children of Abraham. The Lord expects us to take the reins in the struggle for a society that complies with His standards, in which evil is actively fought against. Only if we meet that expectation can we count on His blessing.[166]

Yochanan continued to roar, "I say to you that from these stones God is able to raise up children of Abraham."[167]

What a dark remark, I thought. So does he mean the Lord would be prepared to drop the people of Israel, that he sees the old Israel as passé, that he would consider, or even be on the point of concluding a new Covenant with a 'new Israel,' the 'true Israel'? Does he, albeit less openly, foster the same ideas as the members of the Qumran community? What on earth is the matter with our people?

"Have yourself baptized," I heard Yochanan cry. Again, he repeated those words several times, louder and louder – a born narrator, I thought, a real demagogue. He added, "So that you receive forgiveness for your sins . . . as a sign of the new life."[168] The priest who had just interrupted raised his voice again. "What kind of mysterious babbling is this about baptism as a sign of the new life?[169] Do you imagine yourself as some kind of assistant creator; the Messiah, maybe? You're simply deluding the people. And let me tell you, you won't wash your sins away by immersing yourself in water."

With these words, the men turned and walked away. Various bystanders booed them. Yochanan spat on the ground.

What a spectacle, I thought. One Jew cursing another. Shameful! And what way is that to talk: "brood of adders." They say young adders eat their way through their mother's stomach wall, after which she dies. How dare Yochanan use such terms for our leaders.

I tapped my neighbor's arm. "That Yochanan seems rather an uncouth sort. He behaves the way he looks."

He hesitated before answering. "He does have a rough way of speaking, but he's wise. Baptism is tangible proof that someone has actually changed course. But baptism must be preceded by something, he tells us. We have to start living a respectable life, acting justly towards one another and honoring the Lord, because only then is baptism pleasing in His eyes."[170]

"I haven't heard those words from his mouth, but I can well believe it. I'm clear about the preparatory phase. That washing seems superfluous, to me, though. Misbehavior doesn't reveal itself bodily. If only that were true. Then it would be easily recognizable."

B. OBSOLETE QUESTIONS

By now, Yochanan had clambered down from the stone and was sitting on the ground. He seemed deep in thought and not very approachable. I decided to try my luck anyway and walked over to him.

"May I ask you a few questions?"

"Certainly," he replied, "But first tell me who you are."

"My name is Amos and I've come from Jerusalem. I've come to you for counsel. I'm not satisfied with myself, so I don't feel happy."

"What's the matter?"

"Like you, I'm a Jew, but I'm not sure how to interpret that concept. There are so many interpretations, but which is the right one? I'm a Judean, but I live under a Roman yoke. Does an authentic Jew adapt or does he resist? Is he a dove or is he a hawk? I'm looking for an answer."

"I understand your concern, Amos, but your questions are no longer relevant."

His reply took me by surprise. "What do you mean, Yochanan – if I may call you that?"

"You may. I mean that the current wrangling will soon all be over. Our earthly existence is coming to an end. Our people will split into two. Those who realize what awaits them in time and those who remain the seeing blind and hearing deaf. Those who will enter the new life and those for whom eternal darkness awaits."

"I'm familiar with that view, Yochanan. I've just come from Qumran. The people who live there are obsessed with such thoughts. They, too, wash to cleanse themselves morally. Not once, as you ask people to do, but daily and sometimes even several times a day. But they don't call it baptism. It's not Moses they invoke, but someone they call the Teacher of Righteousness, a kind of Super-Moses. Are you familiar with this group?"

"Yes, I am, and I share some of their ideas."

"Might I say you adopted them?"

"That's an extremely inelegant way of putting it. A mother can bear twins. A specific idea can take root in several people in a specific period of time. I found the idea of a tangible moral cleansing useful. That way, the slate is wiped clean and people can start again with a light heart. That's encouraging."

"That's all well and good, Yochanan, but the Qumran philosophy existed long before your movement began."

"Now listen here, Amos, you didn't come to lecture me, did you? I won't stand for that."

"That's not how I meant it," I said, not entirely truthfully, "But please let me go on." He nodded in assent.

"You say a lot of things. The scope of your words is enormous. They prompt a lot of questions in me. First and foremost this. Why are you announcing your message not in the city, not in the synagogues, but here in the wilderness where no one lives and where only your followers can hear you, whom you've already convinced. The second question . . ."

"Stop, Amos, ask your questions one at a time. Why in the wilderness? Because it is in the wilderness that the Jewish people met the Lord and concluded an agreement with Him. If our people want a new beginning, the wilderness is the place to find Him."

"Clearly, but that doesn't seem very efficient to me, Yochanan."

"You have a rather arrogant way of speaking, Amos, but go on, what's your next question?"

"The men in Qumran invoke the Teacher of Righteousness. Whom do you invoke?"

"You're not only arrogant, Amos, you're impertinent, but your question is very much to the point. I'll answer you. I invoke my father, the priest Zechariah; at least initially; ultimately I invoke the heavenly messenger."

"Could you explain that for me?"

"My birth was a real miracle. My mother had been barren all her life, but then, at an advanced age, she had a child. That was me. It was no surprise. My coming was announced by an angel and that's not all. The angel informed my father that the child would be 'filled with the Holy Spirit while yet in his mother's womb. And he will turn many of the sons of Israel back to the Lord their God and go on before the Lord to prepare his way.'[171] The way to the Lord leads upwards. I see it as my task to prepare the people to walk that path."

Yochanan's tone became soothing. I interrupted him. "I'm wondering whether that path really leads upwards. I can imagine it running horizontally, towards *our* world. That we have

145

the greatest chance of finding Him here on earth. If you keep your eyes trained ahead, not turned upwards, only then will it become clear to you what the Lord considers important. That's how I understand the Sinai Covenant. We mustn't accept there being slaves and masters; those in need not receiving any help; judges flouting the law; injustice flourishing with impunity. Every person is entitled to a dignified existence; that's what the Lord wants. Work to that end. That is your *raison d' être*. Then I will extend My hand to you. Here on earth. Not from heavenly spheres. If you disregard that, Yochanan, then the gates of heaven will remain closed to you – always assuming that such a construction actually exists."

Yochanan thoughtfully stroked his beard and took a sip of water. "You sound very self-assured, Amos. You appear to have a monopoly on wisdom, but don't forget that images can be deceiving. They simply express a personal preference, in your case involvement in current affairs. That's very praiseworthy, but I wonder whether the Lord also thinks pragmatically. What I mean is, He is far above current affairs and thinks in terms of eternity.

In any event, I for one don't rely on notions. They're assumptions. I'm convinced, no . . . . I know that the gates of heaven will open for those who have shown remorse and been baptized by me and it's only for them that perfect, everlasting happiness awaits."

"We evidently have different outlooks on life, Yochanan. I'm seeking the Lord and you believe you've found Him. My purpose is Earth and its well-being; yours is the gates of heaven. You know certainty; I live with doubt. Should I envy you?"

"Ask yourself that, smart Alec. I'm neither a philosopher nor a pseudo-philosopher. I'm a practitioner, practising what I've been instructed to do.

And now, I have to go. I see there's a group of people by the Jordan, waiting for me to baptise them."

"May I come back again?"

"If you like."

He walked off. I walked behind him. Arriving at the River Jordan, he cried, "Prepare yourself. This is a decisive hour in your life. The new life beckons. There is no guarantee that you will enter. You can still slip up. Beware."

The people were queueing up to walk one by one into the River Jordan.

Yochanan stayed on the bank. "Now submerge yourself," he called, adding "I baptise you as a sign of the new life."[172]

Once they had been baptized they climbed back up the bank and thanked him. Most fell to their knees and cried, "The Lord bless you." Yochanan said nothing. His face betrayed no trace of emotion.

I walked back to the place where I'd spoken to him. A little while later, he came back and sat on the ground again.

C. REALITY OR IMAGINATION?

"Those people were visibly moved, Yochanan. It was an impressive ceremony. Evidently, they saw in you an emissary of the Lord. Incidentally, one of your followers told me you're the prophet Elijah, risen from the dead.[173] If that's true, then the Messiah must be coming. Another even believed that you *are* the Messiah.[174] What do you think?"

Yochanan stared into the distance and didn't answer for a while. "You're getting very personal, Amos, and you're touching on a sensitive nerve, but I've never been one to beat around the bush. I'll answer your questions as if you were a good friend. Maybe that's what you will become. In other words, I trust you.

I'm not sure why, to be honest. Initially, I thought, perhaps hoped, that I was the Messiah, but I couldn't convince myself. I can't imagine a Messiah being uncertain of his mission. Surely, a divine messenger would have provided some kind of assurance.

Am I the reincarnation of Elijah? Possibly, but I'm not convinced of that either. Then I wonder if my imagination might have gotten the better of me. Such ideas must be a sign of poor self-criticism. Reprehensible, isn't it? Then I feel rather ashamed of myself." Yochanan was whispering, his head bowed as if speaking to himself.

"Such an idea doesn't just arrive out of the blue, Yochanan; or maybe it does," I added with a certain irony. "There must have been some kind of lead up to it."

"Yes, there was. A little while ago, I had a vision and heard voices. That was when a man from Galilee came to see me. His name was Joshua. A strange character. He looked past me, seemingly absent, turned in upon himself. He asked if I would baptise him, nothing more. I asked him if he had prepared himself. His answer was, 'I have been called.' I asked, 'By whom and to do what?' His reply was, 'To come to you,' and that was all. At that moment I heard a voice saying, 'It is he who should be baptizing you, not you baptizing him.'[175] Did that voice come from inside or from above? I don't know. Anyway, I baptized him. As soon as Joshua emerged from the water, the heavens seemed to open and a dove descended and alighted on him. Was that God's spirit? I heard a voice saying, 'This is my Son, whom I love; with him I am well pleased.'[176]

Once out of the water, I heard the man muttering. He was praying and I heard him say, "God, let me know who I am. Am I indeed Your emissary, a prophet, the Messiah, or a man possessed by the devil? This uncertainty is driving me mad." Then he walked away; where to I don't know. I haven't seen him since.

Were these revelations, visions, fantasies from a man who imagines himself to be called by the Lord? Fantasies born of arrogance? Or had I, indeed, baptized the Messiah? I don't know, Amos. My reason says it's unlikely. Why should the Messiah want to be baptized? Surely, such a role isn't entrusted to a sinner. And why hasn't the Lord informed us in no uncertain terms that the Messiah is coming? Surely, he wouldn't let him appear like a thief in the night.

And yet, my intuition speaks another language. The man made

a deep impression on me. I can't say exactly why. His introverted attitude, his silence intrigued me. He was walking around as if in a dream, in another world. He didn't speak, he sought no contact with my followers, he didn't eat and he even refused to drink. He seemed in a state of ecstasy. He radiated mystery and that fascinated me.

Had I baptized the Messiah? My instinct told me, yes, you did, Yochanan. After all, it's not impossible. In any case, since then I've been sure that *I'm* not the Messiah. The reborn Elijah, then? Maybe. That's as far as I can get."

"So, why didn't you follow this Joshua? You don't mean to say you just let the supposed Messiah walk off, do you?"

"That's exactly it: the supposed Messiah. I wasn't sure. Anyway, I didn't want to let my followers down."

"Surely they would have followed you if you'd made your suspicions known."

"Maybe, but Joshua gave no sign whatsoever of wanting to be in my vicinity."

"Might he have seen you as a possible rival?"

Yochanan's expression hardened, but he didn't answer. I wasn't going to be put off. "You never mention Joshua in your speeches. I can't understand that. Shouldn't that be your core message: the Messiah may already be amongst us? Is it you who sees Joshua as an adversary? Someone competing with you for God's attention?"

"That's quite enough, Amos" snapped Yochanan. Obviously, I'd gone too far. "You're annoying me, boy. Either you don't take me seriously or you're a verbal sadist who likes driving people into a corner."

"I do take you seriously, Yochanan, and no, I don't want to drive you into a corner; I want you to come out of your corner so I can find out what you're really all about."

Yochanan seemed flustered. That surprised me. He seemed so sure of himself when he was speaking to the crowd. No trace of a doubt. "Which has the upper hand for you in this affair," I asked him, "Your reason or your emotions?"

"That depends. It's hard to suppress reason and it keeps interfering, unbidden, in emotional affairs. But the opposite happens, too. The power of emotions can drown out doubt. For me, reason and emotions are inextricably intertwined. But enough of that. I'm not going to say any more."

The conversation was just getting interesting, as far as I was concerned, and I said, "Let me muse on this a moment longer, Yochanan. Just now, when you were talking about the imminence of the final judgement, the approaching end time, you seemed so sure of what you were saying.[177] Was that just show?"

"I suppose you mean am I sure of *that*. You're an intelligent young man. You are, indeed, forcing me to search myself. So now let *me* contemplate this for a moment. I'm certain that I've been instructed to convey this message. I see that as a moral duty: Repent, Jews. Your society is unravelling, threatening to fall apart. Remember what the Covenant you concluded with the Lord on Mount Sinai asks of you. You're trampling it underfoot. The Lord's patience is beginning to wear thin. He's about to drop you.

In that sense, for the Jewish people the end time is approaching. Figuratively speaking, I mean. *That* is my message. In this, I feel like the Lord's spokesman. This, I'm sure of. But whether the end time, a final judgement, is literally around the corner? My intuition knows no doubt, but I'm not certain of it. In short, Amos, yes, I have my doubts; I assume that's what you wanted to know."

Yochanan stood up and began pacing. "I'll leave you in peace," I said quickly, "I can see my questions are annoying you."

D. ALLY OR ADVERSARY?

"One last thing before you go, Amos. You've got me thinking now. You have, indeed, managed to provoke me into reflection.

I'm wondering why I didn't follow Joshua. I already said he walked straight off without a word after the baptism. And that irritated me. Why?" Yochanan answered his own question. "I don't know. Had I expected him to fall to his knees? No. Was it envy? Could I not bear the fact that the voice I heard in Joshua seemed to be my spiritual superior? After all, it should have been him baptizing me, not the other way around. Possibly.

I've heard he's teaching near the Sea of Galilee and that he, too, often talks of the coming end time and of the kingdom of heaven being near. I believe his message is very much like mine. He has a lot of followers, apparently, more than I do. That bothers me. What's more, he doesn't say such nice things about me. For example, I've heard he said that 'among those born of women there is no one greater than Yochanan; yet the one who is least in the kingdom of God is greater than he.'[178] I don't appreciate him making such a remark. I really don't feel that insignificant. Why would the man have had himself baptized by someone so 'lowly.' I've brushed it off, but I have no desire to see him again.

The man made me unsure of myself. Would the Lord have two heralds announcing the message that His kingdom is near? I can't imagine. The message is essentially a message of peace. He surely can't have packaged it in a way that will cause conflict. Deep in my heart, I wonder which of the two of us is the 'long-awaited' and which is no more than his herald. Has one of us maybe been misled, or are we both on the wrong track?"

"I can't answer that any better than you, Yochanan. Don't you find it discouraging?"

"Not at all, Amos, I'm still devoting all my energy to this."

"So, are you saying you believe, but you have your doubts and that doesn't affect your powers of persuasion?" I asked.

"Exactly, Amos, that's just what I'm saying."

"But aren't the two things contradictory?"

"No, they're not. Someone who knows doesn't need to believe, whereas someone who believes has no certainty. False securities dampen persuasiveness. Conviction of faith is a contradiction in terms, a form of self-deception. I'm only now starting to realize that. If you hadn't kept badgering me, I might never have come out of my safety zone. I've got you to thank for that!"

He shook my hand and wandered off towards the river, where a group of people was standing, waiting to be baptized.

E. REFLECTION

I set off again. Alongside the River Jordan in the direction of the Sea of Galilee. So, what did I think of Yochanan? An impressive chap, that's for sure, but a fanatic, scary in the threatening language he uses to describe the fate awaiting mankind. And yet, behind the self-assuredness with which he speaks is doubt, far more than I'd initially suspected.

I hadn't heard him talk about the Holy Scriptures. He seemed to distance himself from explanation, from making statements about God's intentions and expectations.

Had I learned much from him? Not really, apart from that intriguing remark about a certain Joshua from Nazareth. Evidently a man he held in very high esteem: "One who is more powerful than I," he had said; someone who was so much higher that he himself wasn't worthy to untie the straps of his sandals,[179] someone who should have been baptizing him, rather than the other way around.[180] That's quite something. I hadn't expected such servile remarks from someone as soldierly as Yochanan. Veneration unadulterated with jealousy.

I wanted to speak to Joshua at all costs. Might he really be the Messiah? I could hardly believe it. I'd never heard of the man before and, as far as I know, that went for most of us. A Messiah who comes like a thief in the night, unannounced and not unequivocally certified as such by the Lord? No, surely not!

I simply couldn't wait to meet him.

CHAPTER 7

JOSHUA (ALIAS JESUS) OF NAZARETH

Am I actually the 'suffering servant' or am I seeking my own death for the sake of a chimera?

Come aside to me, you untutored,
and take up lodging in the house of instruction.
How long will you deprive yourself of wisdom's food,
how long endure such bitter thirst?
I open my mouth and speak of her:
gain wisdom for yourselves at no cost.
Take her yoke upon your neck,
that your mind may receive her teaching.

The Wisdom of Ben Sira 51:23–25

A. BEWILDERMENT

Arriving at the Sea of Galilee, I turned onto the road to Nazareth. The journey had been long and tiring and I reached the town early in the morning. I really would have liked to get some sleep, but it was the Sabbath and I decided to go to the synagogue first. As I entered, someone was reading from the Torah. The room was crammed. The front section was filled with men only. At the back sat the women, far away from the table on which the Torah scroll lay. So far, in fact, that they could hardly hear what was being read.

Subordination of women – it occurred to me – how in God's

name can that be justified? Didn't the Lord expressly state that He "will have a day of reckoning against everyone who is proud and lofty and against everyone who is lifted up, that he may be abased"?[181] He called on our people to "be holy because I, the Lord your God, am holy."[182] I see regard for one another as a practical interpretation of the concept of "holiness."

I nudged my neighbor. "Is it always as busy as this on the Sabbath?"

"No," he replied. "There are so many people here now because of the rumors that a certain Joshua of Nazareth was coming here today. He's a teacher with lots of followers, but he's attracting a lot of criticism, too, especially from figures of authority. Hush now, though, Joshua has been asked to read the *Haftarah*."[183]

A tall, slim man with black, wavy hair walked up to the front and began to read.[184] His voice was high, not loud, but nonetheless penetrating. He read from the book of Isaiah; a passage in which the prophet speaks of an "anointed," come to proclaim "the good news:"[185]

> To bind up the broken hearted, to proclaim freedom for the captives and release from darkness the prisoners . . . to comfort all who mourn.

Joshua paused, surveying the room with an absent look, then continued, "Today, you have heard this scripture fulfilled."

There was mumbling in the room. People started talking to one another. I heard voices full of amazement at "the gracious words that came from his lips."[186] Others wondered what he had meant by these final words. Could he actually think he was the Messiah? Others pointed out that Joshua had spoken about the messianic time, not about a personal Messiah. Discussion all round. An old man stood up and shouted, "How dare you claim to be the 'long-awaited.' You're the son of the carpenter Joseph of Nazareth. Nothing more than that. You're blaspheming. This is sacrilege in my eyes." He walked angrily out of the room. I

Fig. 8 The prophet Isaiah with a scroll in his hand. This is supposedly the moment when he was called by the Lord. (Isaiah 6:1–9). Relief on the inside of the West elevation of the Abbey Church of Souillac (Lot, France). From: Capoa, de Ch. and Zuffi, S. (2012). *De Bijbel van de kunst. Het Oude en Nieuwe Testament in de Westerse schilderkunst.* [The Bible in Art. The Old and New Testaments in Western Painting]. Milan: Ludion.

Isaiah prophesied that the Lord will punish the people of Israel mercilessly for its sins, but a remainder will be left that has stayed true to Him. They will form the core of a cleansed Israel, heralding a new era in which the nations will know the one true God, live in peace and be lead by a strict, just king, a descendant of King David.
From this text, the rabbis distilled the idea of the Messiah and the coming of the messianic time. Isaiah did not himself use the term Messiah.

think he was a legal scholar. He didn't have the crowd with him. On the contrary. The people started calling out, "Joshua, you worked miracles in Capernaum,[187] healing people. Do it here, in your own city, too. Give your messianic blessing to us, too."[188]

Joshua refused. Why, wasn't clear to me. Perhaps he was afraid his magic powers would fail him in his place of birth. People have to be receptive to a miracle; otherwise it's simply nipped in the bud. Here in Nazareth, Joshua was just an ordinary boy whom people found it difficult to see as an emissary of the Lord.[189]

His refusal made the crowd furious. A small group drove Joshua outside to a hilltop, threatening to cast him into the abyss,[190] but they were stopped in the nick of time.

I had wanted to go after Joshua and ask him to explain, but I sat through the service to avoid being impolite. The synagogue-goers were now slowly shuffling out, talking and gesturing animatedly. Evidently there were some serious differences of opinion.

I waited until everyone had left then spoke to the man who had led the service, a Pharisee teacher I assumed. "May I ask you something?"

"Of course," was the friendly reply.

"Who's the man who read the *Haftarah*? What did he mean by his final words and why didn't you ask him to explain?" My tone was obviously brusque.

"Calm down, now, son," he answered, patting me on the shoulder.

"I didn't ask him to explain because I didn't want to disturb the service. Just exactly what he meant wasn't clear to me, but the impression he gave was that he believes he's the 'anointed' that Isaiah speaks of. The way he directed his gaze upwards and the elevated tone with which he said the words enhanced that impression. There are rumors circulating here that he is, indeed, the Messiah. He doesn't deny it in so many words. On the contrary. He often speaks of himself as the 'Son of Man.' As you know, these days that term is often used for the Messiah.

The qualification 'Son of God' also seems to please him[191] and that term is, without doubt, an honorary title for the Messiah."

My reaction was fierce. "But aren't those ungrounded fantasies, sir? The product of wishful thinking? Why don't you contradict this in the strongest of terms? I mean, you mustn't allow the people to be misled. How, in God's name, could this man liberate us from our oppressors?"

"You're jumping the gun again, young man. There are, indeed, a lot of Pharisees and priests who don't take his pretensions seriously; they even consider them dangerous. For the moment, though, I'm giving him the benefit of the doubt. I don't know. No one knows where or when the Messiah will appear and in what form."

"Perhaps you're scared of making a wrong judgement and blowing it with our possible redeemer."

"That's rather a crude way of putting it, but yes, that's about it. That's quite something to say about someone you know nothing about."

"I don't want you to take it the wrong way, sir, but I do take a stand against what I see as nonsense. I never abandon my reason."

"What I would say, young man, is never abandon hope. Otherwise your reason won't work properly. If you've developed any kind of sensitivity, you must have noticed how strong the messianic longing is in our society. Our people have gone through so much misery. We've lost our freedom, withstood the terror of foreign kings and poor policy on the part of our own leaders as well as Roman oppression; need I go on?[192]

I'm sure you know what the apocalypses are. Scriptures that tell of a prophetic figure who has discovered, through a heavenly messenger, that we will soon be liberated from the evil surrounding us. There's a good reason they're so popular these days. There are a lot of people verbally promoting that message in our land."[193]

"Do you see Joshua as one of them?"

"I suppose so. He talks of the approaching end time, too, about the advent of an entirely new world order. He speaks about a kingdom of God, or a kingdom of heaven, without saying exactly what he means by those terms."

"So he's spreading hope. False hope, I think."

"No, he's not spreading false hope. He's calling on people to repent. Access to the kingdom he speaks of isn't guaranteed. Before the end time dawns, a heavenly court will decide your fate. For those found to be righteous, the gates of the kingdom will be opened. They're destined for a life of everlasting happiness. Incorrigible sinners will be excluded. What awaits them is unending torment."

"Such a prediction inspires fear, rather than hope, I'd say. Fear of being found wanting."

"Not necessarily. Joshua also calls for repentance, for improving your life. Then everything will turn out all right. Surely, that's a message people can relate to."

I was in a contrary mood. During my travels over the past few weeks, I'd become more assertive, reassured that I wasn't spouting rubbish. Well-meant opposition seemed the best way to elicit discussion, even with those in comparison with whom I'm a young novice. I was learning a lot from these discussions.

"It seems like rather an easy way out to me, Master. Showing remorse is all very well, but can that wash a black robe white?"

"That, the Lord will decide, son, not you."

"You know, Master, I recently met another preacher. A certain Yochanan. Do you know him?"

"I've heard of him."

"He's another scaremongering end-time predictor, calling for remorse. But he does more than that. He's getting people to confess their sins then immerse themselves in the River Jordan. He suggests this can wash away their sins.[194] He calls it baptism. Don't you think it's just idle talk? Deception?"

"You're very hot-headed, young man. Think long and hard before you judge. Yes, I know about this. I don't think the ritual is as crazy as all that. Again, it gives people hope. That's crucial. When hope evaporates, a society under pressure sinks into inconsolable apathy."

"I don't deny that. I keep hoping, too. Hoping for what? For a society here on earth, that the Lord can be proud of. Deep in my heart, though, I'm afraid it's just wishful thinking. But you're quite right; it's better to set your reason aside sometimes."

He stared at me in astonishment, shaking his head. "You're a seasoned relativist, young man, and at such a young age. Don't let it go too far. If you analyse a diamond in terms of what it actually is – no more than a piece of rock – then its beauty disappears.

But we digress. We were talking about Joshua, not the so-called Baptist. I don't know if Joshua baptises people, too. I've heard he doesn't do it himself, but his disciples do.[195] I don't know if that's true. You hear so many stories about what Joshua is up to. Some are first hand, although they don't all appear to have heard the same thing, and others are just hearsay.

You asked me what I thought of Joshua. Well, I can't give you a clear answer. I don't know enough about him. He claims a lot of things, but doesn't enter easily into discussion. He gets angry if you contradict him. He's hot-headed, too. My initial judgement is inconclusive. He does say things that are worth listening to. He emphasises God's ethical appeal – respect everyone, regardless of their origins and antecedents – and considers this more important than ritual observance. I agree with him there. A lot of my colleagues could learn from that.

On the other hand, he claims things that raise eyebrows, to say the least, with me and many other teachers. They say he has baptized people, not with water but with the Holy Ghost.[196] That must mean something like blessing with a minuscule fragment of God's infinite Spirit. No man can do that; only the Lord himself. If that's really what Joshua is claiming then it's presumptuous, to say the least.

And there's more. Apparently he said he can forgive sins, but that's the Lord's reserve, as well.[197] And then there's that mysterious claim that he has come 'to give his life as a ransom for many.'[198] We, the Pharisees, but equally the priests, wonder what the man could be thinking. Does he believe he has divine antecedents? In that case we'd be talking blasphemy.[199]

Anyway, I don't know what to think of the man. What I would say is follow him for a while, listen to him, ask questions and get into discussion with him. Try and get to speak to him alone. It won't be easy. Many of his followers see him as a holy man and protect him from anybody wanting to ask critical questions. Well, do your best, young man. I've got to go now. Good luck."

B. LUCIFER TRIUMPHANS?

I left the synagogue with my curiosity whetted. Could this Joshua actually see himself as the Messiah, with a divine background, even? I really wanted to speak to the man, so where could I find him?

I saw two men sitting out front in animated discussion, probably synagogue goers. I approached them. "Do you know a certain Joshua, the man who was reading the *Haftarah* during this morning's service?"

"We heard him, but we don't know him. He's staying in the area around the Sea of Galilee at the moment, accompanied by some kind of commune. These people apparently see him as the Messiah." They began to laugh. "There are quite a few walking around claiming that at the moment," remarked one of them. "Rival messiahs! Applying to the Lord for the job, should I say. He must be having a good laugh about it. Anyway, this Joshua can't be far. Take the road to Kefar Nahum.[200] He generally teaches on the Sabbath and stays at the house of one of his disciples, a certain Peter."

I took to the road and, indeed, the men were right. When I arrived in Kefar Nahum, there was a big group of people in the market square, standing in silence. In their midst stood Joshua. "What's going on?" I asked one of the bystanders.

"During the service, someone was possessed by a spirit, an unclean demon.[201] Joshua's going to drive it out."

In front of Joshua lay a man, his arms and legs thrashing, his eyes wide open and his lips flecked in foam. I watched, enthralled. I'd heard of such sessions, but never experienced one. It was something that hardly ever happened in our circles and any attempts generally failed.[202]

My neighbor nudged me. "Did you hear what the demon said to Joshua? 'I know who you are – the Holy One of God! Have you come to destroy us?'"[203]

I had not heard those words. Was the man imagining it, or was I spiritually hard of hearing? I shrugged off his remark.

Now, Joshua went right up to the convulsing man and said sharply to him, or rather to the demon, "Be silent. Come out of him." The man was still for a couple of minutes, then stood up and walked away looking around him in bewilderment.

"Awesome, isn't it?" said my neighbor. "That man must be blessed by the Lord. He's got the authority and the ability to drive out unclean spirits."

What are you talking about, I thought to myself. "What do you mean by unclean spirits?" I asked, "I consider the spirit to be an essential component of a person. I mean that literally: the spirit is part of his being. It's that person's hallmark, if you like, his personal stamp, the thing that makes him unique, different from all the other individuals walking around in this world. His spirit determines his authenticity. He builds up that spirit himself over the course of his life. By my way of thinking, a spirit isn't something that enters from outside that you can drive out again."

"Are you some kind of budding philosopher? Do you think you can make up your own terminology?" His tone was sarcastic. "I'm more inclined to believe you're an ignorant young man, unaware of the fact that so many other scriptures have appeared over the past few years, in addition to the Torah.[204] Are you aware of them? For many of us, they've changed our view of life. Have you read the works of Enoch or the Book of Jubilees, for instance?[205] They say there was a time when the Lord didn't rule alone in heaven, but surrounded himself with a circle of councillors. Anyone who reads the Psalms already knew it:[206]

> "God presides in the great assembly; he renders judgement among the 'gods'"

It seems that some adjutants became jealous, and started competing with the Lord, even believing they possessed divine qualities. Their leader was Satan,[207] also known as Lucifer.[208] The Lord kicked Satan and his kindred spirits out of heaven. Satan developed into the evil genius in our society: the instigator of evil, assisted by his accomplices. These are referred to as demons or, in the vernacular, unclean spirits.

That's the answer to your question. They strike at the most unexpected moments, make you sick or try to set you on the wrong path. Once you've been possessed by demons, they have to be driven out as quickly as possible, otherwise they destroy you physically or mentally. And driving them out isn't as easy as all that. You have to have been touched by the Lord to get the job done."

"Yes I have read something about this, but I very much doubt that's the way it happened. If a 'prince of evil' actually exists, then why doesn't the Lord destroy him?"

The man shrugged. "I don't know. I'm not one of God's intimate friends. Maybe He has a purpose for him; maybe He wanted to introduce some counterpoint. If we're supposed to strive for good, then fighting evil gives that some sense, doesn't it?"

"I can agree with that, but I can't go along with the idea of a devil who operates independently and from the outside. The devil, evil, is within us. Mastering that, giving good a chance: that's what characterizes the righteous. And then the idea of being made sick by an evil demon! It's ridiculous. Everything that lives can become sick – our crops, our cattle. Is that all caused by demons? Come on!"

The man grew red in the face and even appeared to make a threatening gesture. I wasn't about to be impressed. "So have you read anything in Moses' scriptures about a devil or demons? No, you haven't. The Lord even warns us not to be taken in by 'spiritualists.' He finds them detestable.[209] Surely that says something." The man stalked off without another word.

In the meantime, the square had become packed. There were a lot of sick people, brought by their families on little wagons, quite a few disabled people and plenty of spectators, curious to see how the miracle doctor would go about his work. I was wondering whether Joshua might be more than just a miracle doctor. There are enough of those wandering around in our land, claiming that God guides their hand. A lot of people believe it. I wonder. It could be that their healing power lies in their personal aura. Joshua doesn't call himself a miracle doctor; he says he's a messenger. So who, then, is his master, I wondered.

Two elderly, learned-looking men had come up and were standing next to me. They were discussing Joshua, of course.

"He's a charlatan," said one.

"Possessed by Beelzebub," sneered the other.[210]

"Is that really what you think?" I asked.

"No doubt about it," he replied, "He's out of his mind. That's what his family thinks, too. They even tried to have him locked up."[211]

"Can you really rule out the possibility of him being a messenger from the Lord?"

"Him? The man who calls us, the Pharisees, a brood of vipers and other such colorful things?[212] That doesn't sound so divine to our ears, servants of God's word."

"But our prophets didn't mince their words, either. They chastised our people. Think about Jeremiah, furiously accusing us of turning the Temple into a 'den of robbers.'"[213]

"Prophets, blessed by the Lord, had that right, but not any old miracle doctor."

"You're putting down this Joshua out of hand. You know nothing about the man. He himself seems to have said that he drives out demons 'by the finger of God.'[214]"

"He might well claim that, but he's also said that the demon that's been driven out can come back with 'seven other spirits more evil than itself, and they go in and live there; and the last state of that man becomes worse than the first.'[215] Surely, the Lord would never allow that.

And don't forget, there can be other forces at play, ungodly ones. There are Pharisees who believe Joshua is possessed by Satan, that 'it is by the prince of demons that he drives out demons'[216] and performs other miracles. They're not far off the mark, in my view."

"You're speaking evil, gentleman," I said, "And *that* is ungodly." I walked away.

C. CONFRONTATION AND MEDIATION

By this time, the crowd had spread out. I heard that Joshua had cured a number of people. He'd even apparently brought someone back from the dead.[217] He stood alone, in the middle of the square. Pale, his eyes closed, as if praying.

I walked over and tapped him on the shoulder. "May I speak to you?"

He turned and said, firmly, "No, not now. If you've got any questions, then you can talk to my apostles."

"Your apostles?"

"They're my confidants. They help me spread the good news and I've given them the power to drive out unclean spirits and to heal every disease and sickness."[218]

"Please, Joshua, tell me what the good news is about and who your source is."

"Again, no, not now. Take your questions to Simon, the one I

164

call Peter.[219] He's the one of the twelve apostles I trust most." He hastened away with a big group of people in tow. I joined them. We walked for hours, eventually coming to the Sea of Galilee. Most people put up tents. Joshua withdrew, surrounded only by his confidants. Looked on from a distance, I heard Joshua ask, "Who do people say I am?"[220]

I pricked up my ears. Would he give the answer I expected? "Some say you're Yochanan the Baptist and some the prophet Elijah risen again, or another prophet."[221] Joshua denied nothing. He asked his faithful ones, "But who do you say I am?" Peter answered, "The Redeemer sent by the Lord." Again, there was no denial. He warned Peter and instructed him not to tell this to anyone.[222]

I was amazed. If he were the Messiah, then surely he would unequivocally testify to that and, if he were not, then surely he would categorically deny it? Why this mysterious vagueness? Why was Peter not allowed to say what he thought? Was Joshua scared of Roman reprisals? Was he afraid of not being able to live up to that pretension and, consequently, becoming the laughing stock of the people?

I went over and called, "Joshua! Why don't you reveal who you are? Why don't you allow Peter to speak?"

Joshua jumped up, furious. "Get away from here, rascal. Have you been eavesdropping on us?" Crestfallen, I walked away. I remembered the words he'd ended a lesson with a few days earlier: "Whoever has ears to hear, let them hear."[223] So whose words should I listen to then, Joshua, yours or those of the Torah, or are they in agreement?

I decided to visit Peter. I'd probably blown it with Joshua, but would the simple fisherman be able to answer my questions?

I looked him up the following day. He was a well-built, friendly-looking man, with a thick shock of hair and a black beard. "Joshua referred me to you," I began.

"Ask whatever questions you have, but first tell me who you are," he replied.

"I'm Amos, son of Mordechai, and I've come from Jerusalem. Actually, I've got just one key question. Who is this Joshua and on whose behalf does he speak? I asked Joshua himself, but he refused to answer. Why? Why the mystery?"

"I'll have to disappoint you, I'm afraid, Amos; I can't give you an answer, I can't offer any certainty. Deep in my heart, I'm convinced he's the Messiah. On the other hand, I can't understand why he doesn't clearly confirm that. Sometimes, I just don't understand him and that is all. He recently told us he has to go to Jerusalem, to suffer many things at the hands of the elders, chief priests, and scribes, and that he must be killed, and on the third day be raised to life.[224] I took him to one side at the time and rebuked him, saying, 'Far be it from You, Lord! This shall never happen to You!'

My words weren't well received. He scolded me, saying, 'Get behind me, Satan! You are a stumbling block to me.'[225] I was saddened by his reaction. Sometimes, I can't make head or tail of what he says. Why would the Messiah want to die before liberating us? Who can guarantee he'll return? Why put it off?"

Astonishing, I thought! The man has critical questions, but he doesn't ask them. Slavish admiration, which is dimming his view. I won't get anywhere with this man. Nonetheless, I did ask one more question. "So, on whose behalf does the man speak, Peter? I've heard he claims things that can't be found in the Torah."

"On behalf of the Lord, I've got no doubt about that. The Lord can amend certain statements, can't He? After all, He can change his mind, just like us."

"That sounds like a dangerous thought to me. We'd never know exactly where we are with the Lord."

Peter gave a deep sigh. "Well, I can't give you any more help than that, young man. I'm sorry."

Evidently, we were thinking the same thing. "Joshua is essentially a closed person," he continued. "He's got no patience with people asking questions. We, his followers, his listeners, we enjoy his words like sweet wine. None of us would ever think

166

of expressing doubt, let alone criticism. Me, I'm a simple fisherman. I can't be of any help to you. You'll have to take your questions to Joshua himself."

"Could you put in a good word for me, then? Joshua sent me away; he sent me to you."

"No problem, of course I will, Amos."

Peter' words had made me even more curious. Why was Joshua so defensive? Did he have something to hide?

Peter was true to his word. The next evening, I sought out Joshua's tent. He was sitting eating dry bread, a glass of water in front of him. He seemed deep in thought. Not a good moment for discussion, it seemed to me, but I decided to venture it anyway. "Peter wasn't able to help me, Joshua. So I'm back."

Joshua looked up. "Oh, it's you again, is it, pest, what do you want now?"

"I've got some questions and I'd like an answer."

"You shouldn't be asking, young man, you should be listening, listening to me. Then you will find." He paused. "Peter told me your name is Amos."

"That's right. I've listened to you, but I haven't heard any answer to my question. You didn't ask, but my question is this: Who are you? Are you really the Messiah? Do you speak on your own behalf or on behalf of the Lord? Are you His agent? Why don't you make that unequivocally clear?"

Joshua's face hardened. "Oh, you do go on, Amos. Again, I say follow my teachings and draw your own conclusions. Now go away, you're annoying and disturbing me."

I did as he said. What else could I do? How rude he is, I thought. Does he, himself, have an answer to my questions, though? I decided to stick around, listen and not ask any more questions, however hard that might be.

I listened and heard things I was familiar with. He spoke of the end time and the preceding 'desolation,'[226] of the heavenly court that will pass judgement on our moral weight.[227] I'd read a lot about this and heard about it ad nauseam in Qumran.

He called for support of the deprived, respect for others, whatever their antecedents might be. It was like hearing the prophets of old speaking again. Certainly not redundant sentiments in this era, either. Personal interest is what rules these days. We too often distance ourselves from others; neglect those who merit our attention, while our spiritual leaders promote prioritizing ritual above morality.

What's more, it seemed to me that the man had a way with words. He made masterly use of parables to clarify his ideas. His tone was full of passion and the people hung on his every word. No one asked questions or demanded further explanation. They listened in silent wonder.

I also heard Joshua say things I didn't entirely understand. He stressed that the kingdom of God was coming, but said nothing about where that realm would be. In the domain of the Lord himself? A heaven filled with immortal souls? That doesn't sound very likely to me. Here on Earth, then? An Earth where evil has been vanquished, populated by perfect people blessed with God's spirit? An individual might be able to approach that level, but society as a whole? Nothing leads me to believe this is about to happen. It seems like a wish, a messianic dream.

What I also didn't understand was why he repeatedly said he would be dying shortly, but would be raised to life on the third day.[228] By whom then? And how does he know? And what did he mean when he said he had come to 'give his life as a ransom for many . . . for the forgiveness of sins'?[229]

What sins, I wondered, and would that apply to all of mankind or just a privileged few? And then, does that apply to past sins only or also sins that haven't yet been committed? Does he see himself as a kind of scapegoat, a human version of the animal that's taken off into the desert laden with sins on the Day of Atonement?[230]

I found his behavior remarkable, too. I saw him plucking ears of corn on the Sabbath, together with his disciples. A violation, unless the people were starving, which certainly wasn't the case. When someone pointed this out, he retorted that "The Son of Man is Lord of the Sabbath."[231] Him? Surely that's only the Lord?

He treated the sick on the Sabbath, as well.[232] That is permitted, if the situation is life-threatening or the patient is suffering badly, but these people could quite easily have waited another day.

He ate with sinners, with tax collectors – compatriots who work for the Romans and often also extort money from us to line their own pockets. That angered a number of Pharisees who saw it. He defended himself by saying that he had "not come to call the righteous, but sinners to repentance."[233] That argument doesn't hold water! Joshua's behavior would only have been justifiable if his fellow diners had shown any remorse and they hadn't.

I got the distinct feeling that Joshua was out to provoke our leaders and he was doing a jolly good job of it. He kept insulting them, calling them "hypocrites, a brood of adders, blind guides."[234] But why? It was a mystery to me. You could hardly call that "good news."

Finally, I didn't understand some of the remarks I heard Joshua make and they were also, in my view, inconsistent with our Teachings. I was tempted to think it was blasphemy. He declared all foods clean,[235] in flagrant contradiction of what is written in Leviticus.[236] Who does the man think he is, I thought, a prospective God?

He did nothing to negate that impression. On the contrary. First of all, as I already said, he felt authorized to forgive sins and[237] only the Lord could have granted him such authority, although he didn't claim that. There was more, though. Joshua regularly gave the impression that he was or had been in the presence of the Lord. He claimed that "Anyone who has seen me has seen the Father;" he believed that "all things have been committed to me by the Father" and that whoever publicly acknowledges him before others, the Son of Man will also acknowledge before the angels of God.[238]

In fact, he even suggested that, in human terms, divine blood flowed through his veins. He let slip that he and the Father "are one," that "no one knows who the Father is except the Son and . . . that "whoever believes in him shall not perish but have eternal life."[239] My amazement reached new heights when he talked about the end time again. He seemed to be allotting himself a key role in this, seeing himself "in his Father's glory with his angels . . . sitting at the right hand of the Mighty One . . ." rewarding each person according to what they have done.[240]

At that point, I was unable to restrain myself any longer and shouted – he was quite some distance away – "What on earth do you mean by that? Do you imagine you're some kind of derivate, a kind of human manifestation of the Lord? Have you forgotten that He is unique and indivisible? It sounds as if you're profaning His name!"

I didn't get any further than that before the crowd started shouting me down. "Shut up," they cried, "How dare you? You're the one who's being blasphemous. Get out of here or shut up."

I quieted down. The crowd looked ready to tear me apart. I was angry, but didn't turn away from him. I was finding this Joshua increasingly intriguing. What is it with him? Does he have visions that he takes for reality? Or is he some kind of mystic, passionately longing to commune with the Lord, to merge with Him, ultimately feeling he has done so and recounting his illusions? Or is he speaking in images, in parables, to drum the seriousness of the situation into us? Or should we take his words literally, that he sees himself as an incarnate descendant of the Lord?

On the other hand, he often talks of himself as the "Son of Man." Surely that term contradicts divine origins. In any case, that was true for the Prophet Ezekiel, whom the Lord expressly referred to as *Ben Adam* (Hebrew, Son of Adam), emphasizing his humanity and mortality.[241] But why should Joshua feel he has to do that? Few of us doubted it. Wasn't it more likely, I wondered, that Joshua saw himself as the "Son of Man" described in the Book of Daniel. Joshua knew that book. He'd talked about the end time and "desolation,"[242] a term borrowed from Daniel.[243] What's more, Daniel saw a figure descend from heaven looking "like a Son of Man." He turned out not to be an ordinary man, though. "To Him was given dominion, Glory and a kingdom, that all the peoples, nations and men of every language might serve Him. His dominion is an everlasting dominion which will not pass away."[244] An immortal being, in other words, a super-human redeemer! Does Joshua identify himself with that being? Perhaps he does, but not really a hundred percent. Joshua simply used the term "Son of Man" in the third person as if he wanted to make a distinction between himself and that "Son of Man," as if he is speaking as an alter ego.

Or perhaps I'm way off. Maybe he used the term "Son of Man" simply to refer to himself, instead of saying "I." That's not unusual in circles that see themselves as chic.

Or, perhaps, he really was the Messiah, a descendant of King David, the long-awaited who would turn our land back into an independent nation. A blind man who asked for his help called Joshua "Son of David" and he didn't contradict the term of address.[245] Let me just say that I, personally, have never heard Joshua call himself the Messiah. A Samaritan woman is said to have heard him say it, but that's only hearsay.[246]

Maybe, maybe, but who can be sure? I wanted to speak to the man himself.

D. RAPPROCHEMENT

The next day, I went back to Joshua's tent. He was sitting alone, sunk in thought, clearly preoccupied. "May I come in, Joshua?"

He looked up. His regard was friendly. Evidently, he hadn't heard me shouting yesterday.

"Yes, come on in. You're Amos, aren't you, the young man Peter spoke to me about. You're back, even though I've already sent you away a couple of times. Well, you're certainly persistent. I appreciate that. Stay. What can I do for you?"

"I'd like to know more about your ideas, about who and what motivates you."

"You ask a lot of questions, Amos. I don't know if I'm willing and able to answer them, but go ahead."

Neither of us spoke for a moment. I sighed deeply, feeling tense. "What are you, Joshua? A teacher? A Pharisee? And if so, which school did you go to?"

Joshua looked at me suspiciously. "Your questions are rather direct. What's it got to do with you, I wonder? You're not an accomplice of Pontius Pilate, the procurator, are you? I know he's keeping an eye on me. To him, I must look like a potential troublemaker."

"No, I assure you, Joshua, I'm no traitor. Don't mistrust me, you fascinate me. I'd like to know more about you, hear something about your background."

"You want to know what I am, young man? I teach. So I'm a teacher."

"A rabbi, in other words?"

"Well, that's not how the establishment sees me. I haven't been to any school. They see me, at worst, as an ignoramus from uncivilized Galilee and, at best, as an unauthorized teacher."

"You say that with a smile, as if you don't care."

"That's because I don't. I'm announcing a message. That's my calling. That drives me onwards and fills my life."

"You mean the message that the end time is near, so showing remorse and repentance is in order? But, surely, that message is nothing new."

"You're right, but that doesn't make it any less urgent."

"Is that all there is to your message or does your calling entail more?"

"What do you mean, Amos?"

"Are you plain Joshua of Nazareth, or are you more than that? Are you speaking on your own authority or on behalf of another entity?"

"You're expressing yourself rather clumsily, but do you mean am I the Messiah?"

"Yes, that's exactly what I mean."

"That's what my dear confidant Peter believes."[247]

"You keep avoiding a straight answer, Joshua. Why? Apparently you told Peter you'll give him the keys to the kingdom of heaven.[248] You, yourself, must know more about your own identity."

"You're getting very personal, Amos. Too personal for my liking."

"Well, isn't our spiritual life a personal affair? If you have questions about someone's identity, then you have to manage to get inside them."

"Yes, of course, Amos, but the question is whether they want you to."

"And you don't?"

For what seemed a long time, Joshua didn't answer. Finally, he broke the silence. "I'm an introvert, I don't much like letting others look inside me. I often feel a prisoner inside myself, though, and I have the need to express myself. That's how I feel right now. Perhaps because you've hit a sensitive spot. I'll let you continue. For some reason, I trust you, even though I hardly know you. So far, none of my followers have tried to fathom out who I am or think I am. They expect things of me, they want me to give them hope. That's what they're asking. Just half a word is enough for them to believe I'll fulfil their expectations, their hopes."

"Maybe you only have yourself to blame. You chose your confidants – your apostles – simple, uneducated men."

Joshua ignored my remark and continued, "For most of them I am, indeed, 'the long-awaited.' You're the first who's tried to look further than the surface."

"Thank you for trusting me. I would, indeed, like to know what is beneath the surface."

Joshua glanced up. I realized I was on strictly private terrain now, but, then again, it was he who had broached the subject.

"You talked about your message just now, Joshua; the one about the approaching end time. You say nothing about the identity of the originator. Perhaps he has qualities that make the message even more urgent."

Joshua didn't answer, but looked me straight in the eye. I went on.

"Do you read statements in our Holy Scriptures that might refer to you? I'm thinking about the interpretations circulating within the Qumran community. I was there recently. They think they've read predictions in those scriptures that apply to their community."

Another silence. "Am I being too bold, Joshua?" I asked, cautiously. I got the feeling I was skating on thin ice.

Joshua looked past me. "My answer to your question about possible predictions is yes, or actually . . ." He interrupted himself, "or, actually, I think so. I'm not sure. I've got my doubts."

"Did you, yourself, dig up any statements that might refer to you, or were they pointed out to you?"

"The latter."

"By whom, by a rabbi perhaps?"

"No."

"By whom, then?" I was starting to feel uneasy. How did I dare? Where did I get the courage to confront the man with himself like this? Joshua lowered his eyes, looking apologetic, or was it perhaps doubtful?

"The Lord instructed me. At least, that's what I imagine."

"So are you a prophet of the Lord, His spokesman?"

"That's how many of my followers see me. That's what they believe and hope."

"And what about you?"

"I can't answer that."

"Can't or won't?"

"You're making it difficult for me, Amos."

"I don't mean to, Rabbi; I'd just like an unambiguous answer to a clear question."

"My answer is: Everything is possible for one who believes."[249]

"You're avoiding the issue again. Am I supposed to believe you're a prophet and that, if I believe that, then you *are* a prophet?"

"That's about it. You believe in the Lord, I assume. You've never seen Him, never heard Him speak. We believe He exists and that belief becomes knowledge, internal knowledge, subjective knowledge."

"That might apply to the Lord, but surely you can't compare yourself with Him?"

Joshua's expression hardened. From sadness or anger, I don't know. "Go away, boy, you're getting rude."

"May I come back again?"

"Yes," he replied, then paused for a moment. "I don't know when yet; I'll let you know."

Obviously I'd been too invasive. But to dig beneath the surface, you need a spade. As long as putting me off doesn't mean fobbing me off, I thought.

E. RECONCILIATION

I stayed with Joshua's faithful ones for several days, listening to his daily teachings. They were monologues. People listened breathlessly. There were no questions and Joshua didn't invite them to ask any. His recurring theme was in three parts: the coming kingdom of God, his untimely death for our sins and his resurrection. As what, as whom, he didn't clarify, though, for his audience, it was clear: as the Messiah.

Fortunately, he hadn't been fobbing me off. A few days later, Peter came to say that Joshua was expecting me that evening.

Feeling slightly awkward, I entered his tent again. "Welcome," he said in a friendly tone. I cautiously began with a neutral, impersonal, question. "You often speak about God's kingdom. What should I understand by that?"

"A kingdom under God's direct patronage, Amos."

"I thought He already had the world in His grasp now."

"Yes, he does, but at a great distance. He's delegated its daily management. To us people. We're governed by professional powers: kings, civil servants, military rulers and their subordinates. They're making a mess of it. They're exploiting others, putting financial gain above righteousness: making society into a macabre caricature of what the Lord had in mind at the time of the creation. In God's kingdom, all those intermediaries will be done away with. He'll take the reins himself."

"A social revolution, in other words?"

"Exactly, but not just that: a spiritual revolution, too. People in that new society will have fundamentally changed. Those who've made it safely through the final judgement are beyond sin, as it were.

My ears pricked up. I decided not to insist on what I felt a highly unlikely scenario, but saw an opening for coming back to my key question.

"So, if I understand correctly, you're going to play a major role in that revolution?"

He blushed. "Is that what you've understood?"

"I believe you said as much in as many words. Whoever acknowledges you, you will also acknowledge before the angels of God.[250] You see yourself acting together in your 'glory and in the glory of the Father and of the holy angels,'[251] to separate the (blessed) sheep from the (doomed) goats.[252] There's only one way I can explain those words. You're very close to the Lord.

Is that what you mean? So who and what are you? In heaven's name, please give me a direct answer."

"Well, you're back where you wanted to be, aren't you? You're a skilled interrogator, but, believe me, I deliberately let you go on. Why? Because I need some conversation. As I already said, I trust you; you seem a sincere person. You don't expect anything of me and it's not your intention to put me down on principle, either."

I could feel the tension in me ebbing away. "I'm glad you said that. Yes, I do want to know. I'm not looking for confirmation of rumors."

"You asked who I am. The answer to that question is very simple. I'm an ordinary Jewish boy from Nazareth, born of a Jewish mother, circumcised on my eighth day, apprenticed as a carpenter to my father, Joseph.[253,254,255] Someone without any noteworthy background. I haven't attended any yeshiva,[256] I haven't learned Greek. In fact, I'm a man like many others." Smiling, he continued, "The only unusual thing about me is that I'm unmarried."

"That's an extremely simple answer, Joshua. I'll put my question another way: What are you?"

Joshua became pale, started to play with his fingers and said nothing. I summoned my courage. I'd seen how the question wound him up. "Let me put the question more succinctly than: are you or aren't you the Messiah and, my second question . . ." I hardly dared speak the words, "Allegorically speaking, does divine blood flow through your veins?"

Joshua pressed his lips together and shook his head. When he opened them again, he said, "My answer won't satisfy you. I don't know, or rather: I'm not sure. That's why I forbade Peter to talk about his assumption. I didn't want to get people stirred up. The Roman reprisals would be terrible. Crucifixions by the thousand."

"I don't understand your uncertainty, Joshua. If the Lord decides to send the Messiah to Earth, then surely there can be no doubt as to who is the chosen one. Then He has to make his decision clear to our people and, what's more, answer the question as to why only now. Our people have already been through so many centuries of misery."

"That's not how it happened, Amos. Something happened that turned my life upside down. That was the beginning."

"The beginning of what?"

"Of what has become both a victory march and a martyrdom."

"So what happened? Do you want to tell me?"

Joshua nodded. "A number of years ago, I wasn't yet twenty, I had a dream, one that shocked me and was to determine the rest of my life. I heard a voice speaking to me. This is the voice of the Lord, it occurred to me. I thought I heard him calling me his, 'beloved son' and commanding me to spread the good news and free my people from their sins.[257]

In my confusion, I woke my father. He tried to calm me. 'It's a dream, son. Dreams distort reality. Pay no attention. You're the son of a carpenter from Nazareth. You're apprenticed to him. That's who and what you are. Keep your feet firmly on the ground. I'm your father; who else? The Lord has no sons, only faithful followers.'

I'm going to tell you something. Something I've never told you before. When your mother was pregnant with you, she had a similar dream. She saw an angel, who said to her, "He will be called the Son of the Most High" and "He will reign over the house of Jacob forever."[258] A child of mine! Ridiculous! I said the same to her as I'm saying to you now: Put that dream aside. Forget it!'

But I can't, Amos. Was it just a dream, or was it a dream that predicted something, a dream that would one day come true. Have I been called, the same way Abraham, Moses, Samuel and Isaiah were called by the Lord?[259]

I couldn't shake off the dream and then, eventually, these ideas came to me when I was awake, too. I found it more and more difficult to forget them. My work suffered. Am I, indeed, a messenger of the Lord? But then what's my message? That I have to die for the sins of mankind? Am I some kind of conciliatory sacrifice? I thought everyone was personally responsible for what they did and didn't do. You can't delegate that responsibility. That's what I was taught."

"Dreams usually quickly fade, Joshua."

"Well, not this dream. I ran away from home. I'd heard about a preacher called Yochanan who was practicing by the upper course of the River Jordan and had become popular in a very short time. He was calling on people to repent and show remorse. The end time was approaching; the final judgement was near. There were rumors that Yochanan was the resurrected prophet Elijah, announcing the coming of the Messiah.

I decided to visit Yochanan. He proved an imposing fellow, yelling out his message. Not once, but again and again. It sounded ominous. He was submerging repentant people in the Jordan. Supposedly to wash them clean, morally. You could see how it relieved people. Even though I didn't quite get the point of the ritual, I had myself baptized. When I came out of the water, I seemed to hear a voice saying, 'This is my Son, whom I love; with him I am well pleased.'[260] Did it come from above or from the mouth of Yochanan, or was I imagining it? Was I really that 'beloved son'?"

"Did you start feeling more certain than?"

"Quite the opposite, Amos. Not knowing what to do with myself, I went into the desert. I had no food with me and only a little water. After a couple of days, I collapsed from exhaustion. I couldn't sleep any more. Terrifying images loomed up. A devil came and jeered at me, sneering, 'You, a son of God? Don't make me laugh. Come with me, join my retinue, then you can really make something of yourself.' I wanted to flee, but I was no longer able.

I was rescued. I don't know how. Someone must have come and fetched me. When I came round, I found I was in Qumran, a little settlement by the Dead Sea. I knew a remarkable Jewish sect lived there. You've probably heard of them." I nodded, but let him continue. "They're ultra-pious, Amos, preoccupied with the end time. Preparing themselves by studying the Holy Scriptures, praying and strictly observing the rules for cleanliness. There are lots of rumors going around about them."

"Yes, Joshua, I know." I interrupted him, not wanting to talk about Qumran and eager to go back to my questions. "I know about them. I've been there. They've broken with 'Jerusalem,' they consider our leaders corrupt and the Temple unclean and they've stopped making sacrifices. They believe that they, the Qumran community, are the 'true Israel,' the 'new Temple,' as long as the old one still exists. In their view, study and prayer replace sacrifices. I was wondering whether you picked up any ideas while you were in Qumran."

He thought for a moment. "Well, I wouldn't go so far as to say that. Vague snatches were already floating around in my mind before that, but they became more clearly defined there."

"Which of their ideas struck you most?"

"The significance they attribute to a man they call the 'Teacher of Righteousness.' He taught them to read the Holy Scriptures in a completely different way. There are predictions in them, for example, that apply to their community, which they feel are being fulfilled in their midst.

I wondered who that Teacher of Righteousness was. A heavenly messenger? A prophet? A redeemer? He had passed away, but they expected him to return. How and when was unclear to me. I remember, at some point, an idea occurring to me with a shock. Perhaps I'm that 'Teacher of Righteousness' whom they call God's son, or the Messiah for whom the people have been waiting so long. Maybe I'm the leader of that so-called 'new Israel.' I didn't dare voice the idea. It disturbed me. How dare you think something like that? Remember what your father drummed into you? You're no more than what you are, the son of a simple carpenter.

When I was with them, the Qumran community was studying

the writings of the prophet Isaiah and, in particular, the part that talks of a 'suffering servant' who would be humiliated, tortured and finally killed. But not in vain. He would have 'sacrificed His life for their sins, but rise again.'[261] Am I destined to become the 'suffering servant,' chosen to sacrifice myself for the sins of my people? Me, the carpenter's son from Nazareth? What arrogance! On the other hand, who knows how the Messiah will appear?

The community's way of living was simple, almost ascetic. That appealed to me. But the way they saw themselves as God's chosen people didn't. The Lord is supposed to have predetermined that. I found their complacency objectionable, so as soon as I was strong enough I left; fled, you might even say, more uncertain than I already was about who or what I am."

"I agree with you, Joshua. Their contempt for outsiders offended me, too; it's in flagrant contradiction of the Torah. I did stay there for a while, though, because the way they read the Holy Scriptures fascinated me. And now, here I am with you. What did you do after that?"

"I went back to Galilee. I was resting by the Sea of Galilee, at the foot of a hill when, in the distance, I saw a group of people approaching. It was the Sabbath and they were coming back from the synagogue in Capernaum. Then something strange happened. I stood up, climbed to the top of the hill and looked down. It was as if the heavens wrapped around me like a cloak. There was this intense feeling of happiness and I had the urge to speak. I gave in to it. The words flowed effortlessly from my mouth.

I heard later that I'd spoken in the vein of Isaiah: 'Wash yourselves, make yourselves clean; remove the evil of your deeds from My sight.'[262] He'd comforted the afflicted by giving them a garland instead of ashes.[263] They say I'd promised the kingdom of heaven to the deprived.[264] I couldn't remember any of it.

What on earth did I mean by a heavenly kingdom, I wondered. Surely the Messiah would found a kingdom on earth, under priestly management and God's patronage. A kingdom of God in heaven: isn't that a flight from reality? Were those really my words? I was shocked at myself.

Evidently, I'd touched my audience. I'd made a deep impression on them and a lot of people followed me as I climbed back down the hill. Nobody, not one person, asked me any questions."

"I suppose you expected them to. There was reason enough."

"I asked myself questions, but found no answers. Still, I was starting to get a feel for it. I began travelling, speaking wherever I could. Those who listened started calling me Rabbi. I made a name for myself. I spoke mostly about common decency. Treat your fellow man as you yourself would wish to be treated.[265] That's what the Lord wants. Any other rules come second to that. That attitude will be decisive in the final judgement.

How could I claim such a thing, I asked myself. Where did I get the authority? Surely it can't be mine? I clarified my ideas with parables, amazing myself with my eloquence. Where did I get it from? People were hanging on my every word. My following was growing. I gave twelve of my followers a special position. I called them my apostles. I considered them my confidants.[266]

I didn't recognize myself any longer. You've gathered yourself quite a little royal household there, I told myself. Why so many confidants when one or two might have been enough? Why twelve? Is it perhaps because our nation consists of twelve tribes? Are you trying to construct a new Israel, rewrite the history of our people? Are you making a laughing stock of yourself?"

Not a trace remains of the self-confidence he exudes when he is speaking to his followers, it occurred to me. This is a tormented man. "As I understand it, Joshua, you're critical of your own thoughts but you can't dismiss them."

"Critical isn't the right word. It's because I'm unresolved that I can't shake off these thoughts."

"Doesn't that make you feel anxious?"

"No, it's more a feeling of estrangement, a feeling like there's a second person living inside me, someone I don't know very well, and the two regularly clash."

F. TRIUMPH AND DESPAIR

"In any case, my confidants were honored by their position and not surprised by my statements. Other followers became more awed and more trusting by the day. Many were convinced I was the Messiah. They wanted to hear it confirmed. I didn't say categorically 'no,' because I, myself, was starting to wonder and, what's more, I was scared of falling off my pedestal. I was ambiguous. 'This was not revealed to you by flesh and blood, but by my Father in heaven', I said,[267] referring them to the Lord for an answer.

The crowds and my followers had ever-higher expectations of me: at one point, a man came to me with a scaly skin condition.[268] He threw himself on the ground and begged, 'Lord, if you are willing you can make me clean.' I was at a loss, but I had to do something. I stretched out my hand and said, solemnly, 'I am willing; be cleansed.' A couple of days later, I heard that his condition had cleared up.[269] Now, had I cured the man or was it his conviction that I was a servant of the Lord that had done it? Am I really supernatural or am I a cunning charlatan?"

"You didn't dare mention your doubts?"

"No, and I still don't, even now.

The sick are queuing up for my help. I quickly get fired up as I speak. Words then flow effortlessly from my mouth, becoming increasingly flowery. Sometimes, they call me 'Son of God' and I don't contradict them.[270] You've seen that for yourself. The religious authorities bridled when they heard that. My followers were surprised and shocked at first, but they were soon entranced. I, myself, have become increasingly sure of my role. Sometimes I really feel like the Messiah, possibly even God's 'suffering servant.' Then I find myself in a kind of ecstasy. The feeling doesn't last long, though. It's followed by doubt, even despair. Surely I can't be what I sometimes think I am. I'm fooling myself, me and the people around me. Will I get found out and end up letting down a lot of people in spiritual need? Will this all end in tragedy? I get really dejected when I start feeling like that.

I began having shocking dreams, seeing myself captured by the Romans, feeling myself nailed to the cross, hearing myself jeered at because the 'redeemer' turned out to be fraud. Or maybe it wasn't a dream. Was I already imagining what awaited me as 'God's suffering servant'? Was I, indeed, destined to die shortly?

One dream really upset me. I say a dream, but it might have been a vision or, perhaps, even a revelation. I saw myself seated on a heavenly throne at the Lord's right hand, passing judgement.[271] I told my followers about it. They knelt and kissed my robes in awe. A number of priests and scribes who heard me were appalled. They called me a blasphemer and threatened to drag me before the Sanhedrin.[272] I cringed inwardly, but quickly regained my composure. Confidently, I pulled myself up and said, 'You snakes! You brood of vipers! How will you escape being condemned to hell?'"[273]

"So you've been provoking the religious authorities. Deliberately?"

"No. I only realized afterwards. Had I, myself, spoken or was it an alter ego? If so then who is that other 'me'? I can't answer that.

Increasingly, it was my followers who determined my self-image. I was the anointed one, whom the Lord had sent to Earth. I was to lead them into the Kingdom of God. Some thought that realm would be in heaven, others on Earth. On Earth? Could I, the carpenter's son from Nazareth, oust the Romans? Again, I didn't express my doubts. I said, 'Do you think I cannot call on my Father, and he will at once put at my disposal more than twelve legions of angels'?[274] I had a growing feeling I could no longer disappoint my following.

But was that all? No: often I, myself, believed in my glorious role. I would enjoy it, only to then start wondering desperately if any of this were 'real' or whether I was just role playing."

Such a tragic figure, I thought. Persistently doubting who or what you are can evidently destroy you. So do you have to conquer your doubts at all costs or learn to live with them? I didn't have the answer.

After a moment's silence, Joshua continued, "And yet, when I spoke to the crowds, all my doubts disappeared. I really felt like the anointed one, the Son of God. My self-confidence grew accordingly. I didn't hesitate to call the Lord *Abba* (Hebrew).[275] I started feeling I was part of God's being. That idea shocked me but, at the same time, it gave me an intense feeling of bliss, of happiness, actually. The priests spoke of scandal. Now, the scribes really wanted to have me up in front of the Sanhedrin, but they didn't dare, for fear of incensing the public. The Roman officials kept an eye on me. For them, I was a potential agitator and agitation is a capital offence, punishable by crucifixion.

Yes, Amos, I do provoke them, both the worldly and the religious authorities. You're right. Do I want to die, though? Am I working towards what might be my destiny? Do I have to orchestrate my own death? Is that what the Lord is asking or am I imagining it? Am I pursuing a perverse fantasy? Am I mentally ill? If so, how can so many people believe in me? Can I let my followers down? No! I have to go on. There's no way back now. That's what it boils down to."

There were tears in his eyes. He turned away from me. I took the hint and left the tent. "You can come back!" he called after me.

The next evening, I found him in a pensive mood. "Not now, young man," he said. "I'll let you know when you're welcome again."

That never happened.

G. TOWARDS THE END

Passover was approaching.[276] To celebrate the feast, Joshua went to Jerusalem. He didn't go alone; a crowd of people followed him. Seeing me, he called to ask if I wanted to walk next to him. On arriving at the city, seemingly on impulse, he asked for a donkey with a colt. He rode into the city on the animal's back, with the crowd cheering loudly behind him that the King of the Jews was entering. This caused a huge commotion.[277]

I spoke to him. "How can you do such a thing, Joshua? According to the prophet Zechariah, that's exactly the way the Messiah will make his entrance.[278] You're stirring up the Roman authorities. Playing with fire."

Joshua seemed not to hear me. He rode with the crowd straight towards the Temple Court. As usual, it was full of money changers and dove sellers. When he saw that, he went into a furious rage. Raising his right arm, he balled his fist and yelled, "It is written, 'My house will be called a house of prayer,' but you are turning it into 'a den of robbers . . . You can't serve both God and mammon.'"[279] He smashed up the stalls and chased away the traders. His followers were ecstatic and called out, "Hosanna to the Son of David! Blessed is he who comes in the name of the Lord!"[280]

I couldn't understand Joshua's reaction. Pilgrims from across the border have to be able to change money to buy doves, the sacrificial animal of the poor. Perhaps he'd been influenced by the ideas of the Qumran community.

I could see some Roman soldiers approaching. They didn't intervene, probably for fear of the jubilant crowd.

"What in God's name are you doing, Joshua," I cried again, "You're digging your own grave!"

"I couldn't care less, Amos. Leave me alone." With his head high, he stormed out of the Temple Court, like a proud victor.

Dusk had fallen. Joshua was walking to Bethany, just east of

Jerusalem, to spend the night there. "May I walk with you?" I asked.

"You may. Are you going to tell me off?"

"You're gambling with your life, Joshua. Why?"

"When I was standing by the Temple just now, I had a feeling of triumph like nothing I've ever known. Here was the carpenter's apprentice from Nazareth at the Temple in Jerusalem, being cheered by a great crowd, called on to liberate his people. Roman soldiers making way for him. But then, right afterwards, came the thought: liberated from what? From the Romans? From sin? I don't know. Evidently, I'm in God's hands. I'll be arrested and executed, that much seems certain now. Am I actually the 'suffering servant' or am I seeking my own death on the strength of a chimera? I do get the feeling that my end is near," he repeated. "I must reassure my confidants. They have to continue my mission. I'm going to get some sleep now, Amos, I'm worn out. Good night."

The next day, he went back into town and gathered his faithful followers around him. I'd gone with them, but remained at a little distance.

"Trust in me," he urged them, "Rest assured: if you believe, you will receive whatever you ask for in prayer."[281]

"What do you mean, Lord?" they asked. He ignored their question.

"Friends, let's now sit down to the Seder table and begin the Passover meal."

"May I join you, Joshua?" I asked.

"Of course. We're celebrating the Seder. Everyone is welcome. Not just the prophet Elijah."[282]

I heard Peter say to his neighbor, "We don't need him to come now. He's already here. The Messiah is sitting at the table with us."

We sat down and Joshua immediately began to speak. He announced his death in veiled terms: "I will not eat the Passover meal again until it finds fulfilment in the Kingdom of God."[283]

He spoke again of the coming "desolation." After that battle, he continued, many will prove to be cursed and disappear into eternal punishment, but everlasting life awaits the just.[284]

He spoke in an intense, almost elevated tone. At that moment, all doubt seemed to have disappeared. It was as if he had merged with the alter ego he had mentioned. He was the long-awaited, the Son of God. At least, that's the way it looked.

He broke the unleavened bread, shared it out and said, "This is my body given for you."[285]

How can he say such a thing, I thought. He probably meant it in a figurative sense: may eating this bread instill you with something of my conviction, my spirit. What an offensive image, though! Eating human flesh, in any form whatsoever, was abhorrent to the Lord. He then raised his cup and said, "This cup is the new covenant in my blood, which is poured out for you."[286]

A new covenant? With whom? With him or with the Lord? What a claim! After all, the existence of our people is based on the Covenant the Lord concluded with us centuries ago. Is the Lord putting words in his mouth, or is he possessed by the devil?

After the Seder meal, Joshua and his confidants went to the lovely garden of Gethsemane. There, I spoke to him. "How do you feel?"

"Relaxed but tense, young man. Do I look forward to death with confidence? Yes, I do. I hope and expect to enter God's hand, but dying must be terrible; or will the Lord – after all, he did call me 'His son' – save me from death on the cross at the last moment? I'm calm and anxious at the same time. It seems more like resignation."

No sooner had we reached Gethsemane than we heard the sound of soldiers' boots. "Betrayal!" cried one of the disciples. "Nonsense," said Joshua, "We haven't made any attempt to hide."

H. THE END

Joshua was arrested and interrogated by the High Priest, by the tetrarch of Galilee, Herod Antipas, who was staying in Jerusalem for the Passover Feast, and by the Roman procurator, Pontius Pilate. I heard Joshua had adopted a haughty attitude, refusing to answer their questions and so forfeiting any chance of clemency. The cross awaited him. A terrible death. Was that, indeed, his destiny, or the inevitable culmination of a tragic error?

Pilate's sentence was, indeed, death by crucifixion. Caiaphas, the High Priest, didn't ask for clemency. I'd hoped but not expected that he would; the Romans saw Joshua as a troublemaker, and insurrection in Jerusalem would lead to terrible reprisals. The High Priest is responsible for peace and order in our land. Riots would have cost him his head. I could understand his decision. Better for one man to die than for a whole people to be lost, he'd said.[287]

Joshua was taken away. I walked behind the group. He was locked up in the pretorium, Pilate's headquarters. A sentry was posted in front of the door. Pressing a considerable amount of money into his hand, I said, "The man who was just brought in is my brother. Please let me say goodbye to him."

Eying me disbelievingly, he nevertheless replied, "Okay, but keep it short."

I was led to a cell. Joshua was sitting on a little stool. The sentry remained standing behind me and snapped, "You've got just a few minutes."

Joshua looked up. "You needn't say anything, Amos, let me speak. I'm torn, not by anguish but by doubt. By an internal struggle between hope and despair. This is an unbearable situation, worse than pain. Am I inspired or am I afflicted? A madman who pretended to be God's son but soon fizzled out. A Messiah doesn't die, does he? When he comes, he will immediately put everything right and liberate our land from the oppressors. At least, that's what I imagined. The only evidence I've come across of the Messiah dying is in the Book of Isaiah. Will a Messiah ever actually appear or will he be forever coming? Will the end time ever arrive or is that an ideal to strive for, ever-elusive like the horizon?

I've never known myself. That much is clear now. I've had ideas and seen images that I experienced as real but were, actually so improbable that I was often overwhelmed with doubt. Am I 'God's suffering servant,'[288] or was Isaiah referring not to the Messiah at all, but to the people of Israel?[289] Have I witnessed the Lord, or was it just a mirage? Did he really devise for me the role of universal scapegoat, whose death would relieve mankind of an unbearable burden? Will people who believe in me really be redeemed and face a bright future? Will I really rise from the dead, return and lead people towards that future?

Am I addle-brained, misled by fantastic ideas about my imagined grandeur, or do I foresee a future that is still closed to most people, in which I'm allocated a major role? Those I trusted most fled when they arrested me.[290] Evidently, they realized they were being implicated. Say something now, Amos, I feel so desperate."

I was almost crying and didn't know what to say. "Don't despair, Joshua," I said, "Your followers believe in you; they have virtually blind trust in you. Many of them will say that, thanks to you, they feel like a new man. Their faith in you gives them hope and hope is a powerful elixir of life. Hang on in there! At least something you imagine can then come true.

"Time's up," snapped the sentry. "Let's be having you."

I shook Joshua's hand. "Be strong, Joshua. Don't lose courage. You're a sincere person. That won't escape the Lord's notice, either."

I turned and walked out with the sentry.

The next morning, Joshua was taken to Golgotha, carrying on his shoulder the cross on which he was to be nailed. A great crowd followed him. Some bystanders mocked him, as did the Roman soldiers: "Hail, King of the Jews." Others were wailing and beating themselves on the breast,[291] while yet others looked desperate and called out, "His blood is on us and our children!"[292] What they meant was, may his strength continue to inspire us and our children, which may have fortified him.[293]

He was laid on the cross and an executioner hammered nails into his hands and feet. It occurred to me that the pain must be unbearable. Joshua didn't blink an eye.

I pushed my way forward until I was right next to the cross. I heard him muttering. "'My God, my God why have you forsaken me?'[294] Why don't you do something? If you intended for me to die, then why in this horrific way? Will my death really unburden people of their sins? But which people does this mean? Or is this for mankind as a whole? And what about sins committed after my death? Will I go to Your house, God, or was that house an illusion, or is heaven an illusion, or perhaps forbidden territory for man? Or will people disappear forever when they die? Surely, though, I must be more than a man, God's son. He should possess superhuman qualities."

He saw me standing there and called, almost inaudibly, "I'm so glad to see you, Amos. You've become very dear to me. Help me."

He seemed exhausted. I could barely understand his final words: "Am I awake now or am I dreaming? Am I already dying? I'm so thirsty. The hunger has gone. The pain stays. Is the end time really coming, or will we be stuck forever in the final battle? I don't know. My end time seems to be lasting forever. I'm not sure if I'm the long-awaited. In any event I never became a qualified carpenter. Does my life remain incomplete? I'm going to close my eyes and try to rest. I'm so afraid I've thrown my life away."

He closed his eyes. I called up to him, "Now you, yourself, must believe, Joshua. Believe that, after your death, there will be people who continue to believe in you and draw strength and hope from that belief. With that belief, your life and suffering will have not been in vain. 'Everything is possible for one who believes.'[295] Those were your own words."

There was no answer.

I. REFLECTION

I walked back home, drained and in shock. How terrible the death struggle is. Perhaps this is the final battle the apocalyptic preachers keep talking about.

My father opened the door. He looked at me. "What's the matter, son? You're so pale. Your face is stained with tears."

"I just experienced a crucifixion from close up. It was Joshua. You know: the preacher there's been all that fuss about."

"He was controversial, Amos."

"I know, Father, but his death was terrible and, what's more, unnecessary. He provoked the authorities, sowed unrest in Jerusalem and loudly proclaimed that the Temple would be destroyed.[296] It was as if he were tempting death."

"Calm down, son, have something to drink, have a rest. I'll leave you alone for a bit."

About an hour later, Father came back. "Did you learn much from your discussions with Joshua?"

"More than anything, Father, I learned about people, saw that doubt has two sides to it. It encourages self-examination, stimulates internal dialogue and so enriches our existence. But doubt can also prompt an internal struggle that destroys your life."

"What did you think of the man?"

"A really complex character, Father. Fascinating yet paradoxical, dangerous and tragic."

"What do you by that mean, son?"

"He's – or, unfortunately, was – first and foremost a fascinating, passionate speaker, eloquent and with a masterly use of parables for clarifying his claims. I found his vision of our Teachings contradictory, to say the least. On the one hand, he stated that until heaven and earth disappear, not the smallest letter, not the least stroke of a pen, will by any means disappear from the Law.[297] On the other hand, he flouted that Law without blinking an eye. He declared all foods clean, he was lax with the Sabbath laws, ate with sinners even if they hadn't shown any remorse and, even more mysteriously: he made statements that seemed entirely contradictory to everything I heard at school. I'll give you a couple of examples. He felt he had the right to forgive sins, claiming to be lord of the Sabbath. He implied he would be some kind of magistrate at the last judgement.[298] He suggested that, for those who have faith and don't doubt, everything would turn out all right.[299] Believe in whom, though? The Lord? That would be a platitude. In him? If so, in what capacity?

Another time, he remarked that 'whoever wants to save their life will lose it, but whoever loses their life for me will find it.'[300] What did he mean by 'finding life'? Did he mean everlasting life? Did he think he could guarantee that? So did he think he really was a key figure in God's entourage, always assuming He has such a thing?

In other words, Father, he made promises he couldn't keep even if he really was the Messiah. The Messiah will be a man, no more than that, blessed by the Lord but without His capacities. At least, that's what I learned.

Or, maybe, Joshua thought that the Messiah would not be a son of David but his superior, someone with a rank just below that of the Almighty, perhaps His agent or deputy, possessed of divine authorities. Perhaps Joshua felt he'd been allotted that role.[301]

Suggestions and allusions are what I heard, Father, but no definitive statements. An unfathomable figure. I can't put it any other way.

I called him dangerous, too. First and foremost because, without any spiritual qualms, he upended our constitution and made promises that seemed rather empty to me.

Secondly, because he suggested, or at least failed to categorically deny, that he was the Messiah. That stirred the people up, put them into a state of ecstasy, a mood that could easily have led to a revolt against the Romans, with dire consequences: crucifixions by the thousand.

A dangerous and, at the same time, deeply tragic man. Desperate, I mean desperately torn by doubt. Self-assured on the outside, bold, bordering on the audacious – a man with a mission – and, on the inside, a man unsure of his identity, unsure whether his ideas represented the generally-applicable world or an imaginary world. Who am I, he wondered: Joshua, the son of Joseph the carpenter from Nazareth, or my alter ego, God's kin, perhaps even His 'suffering servant'? He was determined to be crucified, provoked the authorities. Deliberately, hoping or perhaps even expecting the Lord to miraculously intervene. Well, that's not what happened and he felt hopelessly lost, a failure.

Occasionally, I wondered, 'is this man nuts?'"

"That's a bit strong, son. Anyone can dream. The dream of being close to the Lord, merging with him, as it were, is not uncommon. That dream can become concrete. Then you start believing it really is the case and the dream becomes an experienced reality. That's not nuts; it's a manifestation of imaginative power, some say of unbridled imaginative power. It can create an intense feeling of happiness. But only temporarily. It passes.

If I understand you correctly, Joshua lived in what you saw as an illusionary world."

"Sometimes, Father. He fluctuated, living alternately in two worlds, the real one, in our reality, and then in an imagined reality – for me and for many of us, I think – an illusionary reality. He wasn't sure which one was the true reality. For him, the primary stabilizer for our existence – our identity – was extremely shaky. Periods of happiness alternated with bouts of deep despair. It was that despair that dominated the final part of his life. A Jew in spiritual need, Father. Tragic. The Torah was given to our people not to obscure life, but to lighten and enlighten it."

"Quite so, son, but for that you need both feet firmly on the ground. If your imagination runs wild, then you risk finding yourself in a vacuum, a world filled with illusions."

"I don't think that's so for Joshua. As I said, he fluctuated between two worlds, the common world and his private world. That's one thing. The other is your choice of words. Illusion implies that the content of the illusion is false and I'm not sure if that applied to Joshua. Delusion or reality? We don't know. Perhaps no one will ever know; it will remain a mystery forever. So I take back the word 'nuts.'"

"Did he discuss his problems with our teachers?"

"Not really. There was some brief contact with the Pharisees, but that led almost immediately to arguments. Joshua turned out to have a short fuse, he was easily riled. Our authorities decided without much ado that this was blasphemy. There was a lack of mutual respect and interest. A dialogical debacle, Father. I wonder why the man didn't get a lengthy, thorough hearing on his views."

"Wasn't he brought before the High Priest and the full Sanhedrin, then, Amos?"

"I think that's highly unlikely, Father. You can't get the seventy-one members of that Council together at such short notice. What's more, most of them would probably have excused themselves due to preparations for the approaching Passover Seder. But I don't know how the proceedings went. I mean, Sanhedrin sittings aren't public, are they?"

"But Joshua was condemned to death, or at least that was the advice given to the procurator. Surely, only a full Sanhedrin is authorized to do that?"

"I think that only applies to *Halakha*-related [302] issues, not when it comes to a clear case of incitement. Anyway, the procurator wouldn't have needed a recommendation. The Roman authorities nail rabble-rousers to the cross. Full stop. They don't need an extensive procedure for that."

"But he, himself, claimed to be the Messiah, didn't he? Isn't that a *halakhic* affair?"

"He, himself, was highly uncertain about it. I already told you."

"You might say so, but he reputedly claimed as much to the High Priest."[303]

"Some of his followers claim as much. Others say he gave an ambiguous answer, though: 'You say that I am.'[304] Neither one thing nor the other. Incidentally, even if he had admitted it, the High Priest wouldn't have been particularly bothered. These days, there are loads of people who think and act like that. It hasn't cost any of them their lives. Joshua incited unrest. That's why they condemned him. Was he trying to unleash a popular uprising? He did, apparently, say that with God's help he 'could liberate Israel.' Or had hope become expectation for his followers?[305] I don't know, Father; he wasn't clear on any of this, either."

"You know, Amos, I wonder why the man didn't set up a school in Jerusalem. There are so many here. He could have put forward his ideas for discussion."

"He was inspired, Father. He felt he had a message. He wanted to announce it, not discuss it."

"You have to discuss everything, son, even God's word. His word is no longer in heaven; He said so Himself.[306] The Torah belongs to all of us. In a manner of speaking, it's given anew every day. We're a people of questioners, for whom each answer generates a new question."

"Doesn't that create a labyrinth?"

"You've got your whole life to find your way through it, Amos.

Well, anyway, son, I advise you to take one more journey, a long journey, to Alexandria in Egypt. There's a scholar there named Philo. He's attempting to bring our Teachings and those of the Greek sages together, to reconcile them. He's unpopular with our teachers, too. In their view, he's a Hellenized Jew[307] and therefore a danger to the purity of our Teachings. I'm not so worried about that myself. The Greek and Hellenized world is rich; rich in thinkers, poets, architects, sculptors . . . you name it. No sense staying cooped up inside with the shutters closed when the sun's shining outside. That way the house starts to smell musty. Get outside, but keep your house in order."

"But, Father, that Greek culture also has an anti-culture: those awful gladiator fights, the debauched bacchanals honoring some of their gods, such as Dionysus; their perverse focus on the body, particularly the male body!"

"Yes, you're right, but don't forget that each culture has its constructive and its destructive components. After all, it's a human product. Anyway. Go to Alexandria and try to speak to Philo. Get an impression of his ideas.

I've got a friend who does business in Alexandria. You can travel with him and I'll pay for your journey. I've got no idea whether Philo will see you. He's a man of high esteem, a member of a high-priestly family and a leader of the Jewish community there. Do your best, Amos."

"Fantastic, Father! They say Alexandria is the place to be for new ideas, that it rivals Athens and Rome in that respect. I'm really grateful.

Take good care of yourself, Father, I need you!"

POST SCRIPT

I would like to say two things to clarify the above.

1. In this discourse, Jesus has been "de-theologized." Amos, the man who talks to him, is a contemporary and, for his Jewish contemporaries, Jesus was a fellow Jew, a charismatic teacher, but no more than that. He was attributed the divine aureole only later, in the early Christian world.

At the *yeshivot*, the Jewish schools, the divine rules were extensively debated and there were major differences of opinion. The point of departure for such discussions was, however, clear: the Torah was the constitution given by the Lord and revealed to the Jewish people on Mount Sinai.

That constitution was founded on two pillars. First and

foremost the uniqueness and indivisibility of the Lord and, secondly, the absolute separation of the heavenly and earthly realms, of the sacred and the profane. To put it metaphorically: no one could see God's face and live. Even the greatest prophet of all time, Moses, only saw the Lord's back (Ex 33:23). After all, one cannot look at the sun without being blinded.

2. Nothing is known with any certainty about Jesus' life, let alone his internal life.[308] My treatment is fiction. Is it pure fantasy? I don't think so. His ideology must have prompted serious doubts in Jesus the man. Am I really who I think I am? In him, I see a man persecuted by doubt.

Does that diminish his significance? Not in any way. To my way of thinking, uncertainty and doubt are the essence of religious belief. "Don't take life for granted" and, for the Jew "don't take the Torah for granted." Don't neglect to question the point and meaning of your existence, your whole life through. Certainty of faith leads to what I have called "faith coagulation." in my book *God en Psyche. De Redelijkheid van het Geloven* [God and Psyche. The Rationality of Believing]. In this discourse, when I paint Jesus as a doubter, that should not be interpreted as an attempt to devalue his significance. On the contrary, it raises my esteem for this great Jewish prophet.

Does my knowledge of the human soul and its emotions play a role in the aforementioned assumption? Most certainly. In doing so, am I psychiatrizing the figure of Jesus? Certainly not. Jesus' ideas were, to some extent, unusual, even for the time and the community in which he lived. They were outside the statistical norm. In that sense, they were abnormal. This term is not, in any way, used in the sense of unhealthy. Does this not undermine the significance of Jesus? Not at all. Abnormal psychological phenomena can impoverish and restrict a personality, but also enrich and expand it. In the aforementioned book, *God and Psyche*, I have categorized these abnormal, but constructive psychological phenomena as creative psychopathology. They are the product of a fertile imagination. Great visionary artists, great visionary scientists and great religious thinkers derive that greatness from their ability to reach across the bounds of reason and enter the domain of imagination. Without imagination, scientific, cultural and religious life stagnate.[309]

Fig. 9 The library of Alexandria, one of the greatest in the ancient world. At the time of Philo, as a centre of culture and science, Alexandria could compete with Rome and Athens.

CHAPTER 8

PHILO OF ALEXANDRIA
(ALIAS PHILO JUDAEUS),
CHAMPION OF HELLENISTIC JUDAISM

"I hope that, from your side, you'll reflect on the points of which you've been critical, Amos. You don't need to embrace them to acknowledge them for what they are: tools for preventing spiritual ossification."

For the bewitching of vanity obscureth good things, and the wandering of concupiscence overturneth the innocent mind.

The Wisdom of Solomon 4:12

A. THE "UNCREATED"

The voyage to Alexandria went smoothly and my morale was high when I disembarked. I needed it. This wasn't Jerusalem; it was a metropolis. The people didn't speak Hebrew or Aramaic; they spoke Greek. I can understand Greek, but I don't speak it very well. There were temples, quite a few in fact, but none dedicated to the Lord. I couldn't find a priest to give me directions and I didn't know my way around this city. The problem didn't take long to solve, though. I saw a lot of people walking around with *tzitzit* on their kaftans. [310] I asked one if he knew where Philo lived. He did and, surprised, asked, "Are you going to visit him?" He followed that sarcastically with, "I'm sure your visit is just what he's waiting for."

He showed me the way and, after some searching, I found

Philo's house, a magnificent property surrounded by a large garden. Impressive, I thought. As an anonymous young man from Jerusalem I hope I won't simply be turned away. That was immediately followed by another thought. I'm not a nobody. I might not be a hereditary aristocrat, but I am someone with the ambition of becoming a member of the spiritual elite. I had come to this conclusion during my travels. I had the guts to enter into dialogue with this wise man. If only they'll let me in!

I rang the bell. I waited a long time until an old man came out. He didn't open the gate. "What do you want here?"

"I would very much like to speak to Philo."

"It's not as easy as that, young man. You have to write him a letter, stating who you're and what you want of him. There's a long waiting list, I can tell you."

"I've come all the way from Jerusalem, sir. My name is Amos and I can put what I would like to discuss with him into a few words: what is Jewish identity? What should a Jew's 'inner self' be like? Could you tell your master that?"

The man shuffled back into the house and came back shortly afterwards. "The master said, 'That's a question that's been bothering me, too, all my life. Let the man in.'"

I followed the servant up a monumental staircase to a big room filled with foliants, a few chairs and a big table, at which a man sat working. So this is Philo: a handsome, finely-chiselled head, intelligent and friendly-looking. Well, I thought, at least he doesn't look like a narrow-minded high-flier.

"Sit down, young man. What's your name?"

"Amos. I'm the son of Mordechai, a Jerusalem silversmith." I was nervous, nonetheless, and a little awed: such a sculpted head, his heavy, sonorous voice and, naturally, his reputation.

"I heard you're struggling with an essential question. Such questions are seldom asked. Evidently you're a thinker. That could take you places. Do you speak Greek?"

"Not very well, Master."

"Then we're quits. My Hebrew is poor. I speak mainly Greek, but with God's help we'll get by."

I decided to come straight to the point. "With God's help? I suppose you mean that figuratively, in a manner of speaking."

"No, that's not how I mean it. I mean it literally."

"You mean the Lord bothers himself with this kind of minor detail?"

"I'm not talking about the Lord himself; I mean man, a creation blessed with reason, the capacity to think logically. With creative ability, in other words. You can interpret that ability as a spark of divine reason; the divine reason that constitutes the origin of creation.[311] Creative ability enables man to turn the impossible into the possible, to create something out of nothing."

"I don't get what you mean, master. You use such difficult words!"

"I understand that, Amos, I threw you straight in at the deep end, when you'd only just tested the water. I'll come back to that later. For now, though, let me just say: that 'divine spark' will help us get through this conversation. Anyway, what brings you here?"

"First of all, I'd like to thank you for seeing me, a man without any reputation, an unknown who just turns up unexpectedly."

"Don't stand on ceremony, just get to the point and make sure your questions are interesting."

"I'll start with a question that I didn't come to ask. When I arrived, I heard music playing. A flute, I think."

"Ah, that was my children. They play a lot. And it pleases their old dad. I listen while I read Moses' scriptures."

"Doesn't the music distract you?"

"On the contrary; I concentrate better and it helps me think more profoundly. For me, music is the link between the natural and the supernatural, the human and the superhuman."[312]

"Does it bring you closer to the Lord?"

"Yes, it does."

"So you do believe in His existence, then?"

"What a question, Amos!" cried Philo.[313] When you see a painting or a sculpture, don't you wonder who its maker is? If you arrive in a well-planned, well-organized town, then doesn't that mean there have to be wise administrators?[314]

As I said, what a question! What Jew doesn't believe in the unique, indivisible God? Without that belief you're not a Jew. A Jew without that acknowledgement is an empty shell, even if he is, in a formal sense, a Jew."

"But that shell, in itself, is not unimportant, is it Master? It incorporates our own land, our common language, our customs, our shared history. Surely these things help determine an identity?"

"To a limited degree, boy; after all, those characteristics are largely unstable. Take us here, Jews in the diaspora, we no longer speak Hebrew; we speak Greek. Many of our habits are borrowed from our hosts. We don't share a past with the Jews in Judea and the two pasts will diverge even further in the future. The contents of that shell, the Torah, the trust in God's word, the observance of his guidelines: that's what determines our identity. That's what distinguishes us from other peoples."

"So what about those other peoples, then? Do you see them collectively as empty shells?"

"Not empty shells, but shells with the wrong content, filled with a collection of counterfeit gods. One day, though, they, too, will come to know Moses' universal laws and, consequently, those of the Lord. It's no coincidence the Lord spoke to us in the wilderness, in no man's land, rather than in the Promised Land. This was the Lord showing us that His house is open to all peoples.[315] The Lord will receive those who come over with open arms and we'll do likewise."[316]

"You speak condescendingly of counterfeit gods. Is the idea of one invisible, omnipotent Creator so logical? Shouldn't we conclude that we don't know how or by whom the world was created?"

Philo looked amazed. "I hope you're not one of those people

who believe in neither God nor idols. Atheism is the greatest of all vices."[317]

"No, Philo, don't worry, I'm not an atheist. I'm just sounding you out, trying to find out what you think."

"Moses made us aware that our world was created and that the Creator presides over everything that has been created.[318] He created order from chaos. The cosmos had a beginning and the one who gave the cosmos its starting signal was the Lord.[319] He is omnipresent but exists in neither time nor place. We will never understand that paradox. He has no beginning and, for Him, there will never be an end.[320] I call Him the 'uncreated.'[321] That, Amos, is the alpha and omega of our Teachings, is it not?"

"Yes, of course, but certainties can be debated, too. Certainties aren't inviolable."

"Plenty of things are debatable, but not this. A creation without a Creator is a logical impossibility, at least to my way of thinking."

"You said just now that He, the Lord, has no beginning and no end. That doesn't apply to the world, though, does it? The world has a beginning. Do you think the world could also come to an end, that things could ultimately go wrong with us, that He could decide that his experiment with mankind and the world has been a failure, that evil has spread ineradicably and the game is now over for good?"

"I don't think that can be ruled out, unless we succeed in dramatically revising our way of living and the structure of our society."

"So, do you see yourself as an apocalyptic?"

"No, but I do believe in the possibility of an Armageddon, of a global conflagration that could lead to the demise of the world. Provoked not by the Lord, but by us, ourselves, due to our intolerance, our inability to follow His will, His laws.[322] The Lord will weep, in a manner of speaking, at such a catastrophe. Experiment failed!"

"That's a pretty gloomy prospect."

"Don't get me wrong, Amos, this is a possibility, not a certainty."

"I believe we Jews have an optimistic view of the future, that we cherish the hope that, eventually, a messianic time will dawn in which an end will come to all our misery. A time in which we will 'beat our swords into ploughshares and our spears into pruning hooks. In which nation won't take up sword against nation, nor will they train for war any more.'"[323]

"I share that hope, Amos,[324] but don't forget that no guarantees have been given. The Lord can always decide to reverse a decision."

"Do you believe the Messiah will herald that time?"

"No; its coming will depend on us. We, ourselves, will have to repair our world. With God's help, of course. If we turn collectively to the Lord, then He will welcome us.[325] Remember, Moses never talked about the coming of a Redeemer."

"So you think it's possible the world could cease to exist. In that case, does the Lord disappear from the scene as well?"

"No, Amos. I already said: He is timeless and eternal; He will always be there, with or without our world."

"Wouldn't it be better for Him to put a stop to the experiment with this world now? Think of a new set up and start all over again?"

"I assume that remark is meant as a joke. A tasteless joke, in my opinion. But I'm getting hungry. Let's leave it there for the moment and get something to eat."

B.   ORIGIN WITHOUT ORIGINS

Philo rang the bell and a servant brought in some food. "Have you got somewhere to stay while you're in Alexandria, Amos?"

I shook my head.

Philo addressed the servant. "Could you go to Levi and ask him if he can offer Amos his hospitality?"

Turning to me, he said, "Levi is a good and learned man. He knows what virtue is."

We ate without saying much. At some point, I began again. "You speak so freely of the Lord. You've evidently formed a clear picture of Him, Master. Could you tell me something about it? That's what I'm looking for."

"I haven't formed any clear picture of the Lord and, by the way, don't call me Master. I'm neither a potentate nor a teacher. Call me Philo.

I've struggled with the image of God and I'm still struggling with it. With the Greek philosophers, I encountered an image of the Creator that's quite different from ours. They see the creator as an anonymous, impersonal abstraction; a master designer, but one with no interest whatsoever in the results of his design. He couldn't care less about our world, in other words. He's seen as the origin of everything, without himself having any origins. A constant quantity, void of any human attribute. This god is reminiscent of a force of nature or, to put it another way, of all the forces of nature. Such a conception is, certainly, majestic and impressive, but it's at best distant and inaccessible. An icy statue, with which no relationship is possible. That's certainly not the image we Jews have of the Lord. You know that."

"Yes, I know that, Philo, but at the beginning of the creation he is, nonetheless, introduced in a somewhat similar way. As *Elohim* (Hebrew),[326] the Creator of heaven and earth who, himself, remains at a distance; an impersonal, nameless entity who gives the impression of not being concerned with His Creation. That doesn't differ much from the Greek image you're describing."

"That's as may be, Amos, but He quickly adopts another attitude. He gets involved with His Creation, becomes approachable. Increasingly, he becomes *Adonai* (Hebrew),[327] an empathetic father figure, a super father, compassionate, just, loving, but also demanding, strict, moody, and sometimes incomprehensibly ruthless.[328]

Two images of God, both immaterial, but contrary. You could

even say contradictory. The Creator as an anonymous, omnipotent force of nature that is dear to the Greeks, at least the philosophers amongst them and then the superhuman, but still a recognizable father figure, concerned with the ups and downs of mankind, who is so dear to the Jews but not recognized in circles of Greek thinkers.

Lack of recognition means lack of comprehension, alienation, mutual animosity. Not exactly fertile ground for peaceful coexistence."

"A transcendental God who manifests himself in two forms seems like a logical impossibility. Is that what you're saying, Philo?"

"Yes, it is. I was wondering if the two interpretations might be reconcilable. Both appeal to me.[329] I didn't want to make a choice; instead, I wanted to bridge the gap. I've never claimed to be capable of a synthesis."

"Fascinating, Philo. Would you like to tell me more about it?"

"Absolutely, but not now. I've got some work to do. You can come back tomorrow evening if you like. Ask the servant who takes you to the gate to show you the way to Levi's house. Good night."

"Thank you, Philo."

C. APPEARANCES

Levi's house was in the middle of the Jewish quarter. He had a function, that of *gabbai*, secretary to an organization that supports the poor and needy.

Levi met me at the front door. "It's quite a privilege for Philo to see you without a prior appointment. He doesn't do that for everyone. He gets far too many people coming to the door for advice or support. You must have made a good impression."

"I'm glad to hear it. He's such a knowledgeable man and a really good listener. That's a rare combination. You must be very proud of him."

"Aren't we just. He's one of our most important leaders. He has a place of honor in our synagogue. And that's saying something!"

"Your synagogue? You have synagogues here?"

"Yes, lots, one in every neighborhood. As you know, in Alexandria we don't have a Temple like you do in Jerusalem. Here, the *yeshivot* (Hebrew)[330] have become God's houses. Worship services are held there, too."

"So, without priests and without sacrifices?"

"Exactly. We study the Holy Scriptures, pray together and seek a personal relationship with the Lord instead."

"Who leads these meetings?"

"Anyone we consider learned enough. These meetings – we call them services – are what binds our community!"

"You live a good and fairly carefree life here if I'm not very much mistaken. Do you feel completely at home here, or is that just an impression?"

Levi sighed and paused for a moment. "I can't give you a firm answer. Yes and no. Yes, in as much as the Roman authorities have accepted that we live the way we do. We have our own houses of worship, our own courts that act when Jewish laws are violated and a council of seventy-one elders that manages our internal affairs, like the Sanhedrin in Jerusalem.[331] We don't have to honor any of their gods, not the city god, not the emperors they've endowed with divine qualities. That's of cardinal importance. Offerings are made to them during every feast, and at every sporting event and we're exempt from that, but that privilege also has its disadvantages. It means we can't fulfil any public functions and full Roman citizenship is withheld.[332] We're not seen as real patriots.

That's not all, though. Now I'm coming to the 'No.' I don't feel accepted here. We've remained foreigners, actually. Our veneration of one invisible God, preoccupied with morality, is seen as a ridiculous superstition. They don't understand our dietary customs. Circumcision is seen as a barbaric mutilation of the body. The fact that gentiles are considered to be ritually unclean and our women aren't allowed to marry gentiles is seen as an insult. Our way of life clashes with the Greek ideal of an ecumenical, multiracial and multicultural society. What's more, the economic prosperity of rather a lot of Jews is a thorn in the side or our gentile co-citizens. Outsiders who are flourishing!

And then there's this. Each year, we Jews in the diaspora donate half a shekel for the maintenance of the Temple in Jerusalem and the well-to-do often give far more. That doesn't go down well, either. That money should have been destined for the temples of Zeus and other gods.

In short, we are not seen as one of theirs, by either the Greeks or the Egyptians. Despite the fact that we've been living here so long and contributed so much to helping this city prosper."

I listened, fascinated and amazed. "I've got two questions, Levi. One is factual: how long have Jews been living here? The other is emotional: to what extent are Jews here affected by all that awkwardness?"

"I can only answer one question at a time, Amos. The first one first. Jews have been living here for a very long time, since the city was founded by Alexander the Great.[333] The idea was to make Alexandria into a big commercial port and that's what it became, partly thanks to us. At the time, inhabitants for the city were recruited, or rather imported, from Greece and from conquered territory, a lot of Jews from Judea, in particular. They were persuaded or, actually, forced to leave. Many followed later, of their own free will. Judea was gradually becoming overpopulated and the Hellenization of the entire Mediterranean area was offering great economic opportunities. Jews bought land here, grew grain and started to play an important role in its transport. We were amongst the real founders of this city. Now there are lots of us; some say a million,[334] although that may be a slight exaggeration.

And now your second question. To what extent are we affected by that, shall we say anti-Judaism, in daily life? Well, in the pre-dominantly Jewish neighborhoods, very little, of course. Out-side of those neighborhoods, though, it's quite noticeable. Your presence is remarked upon and not always appreciated.[335] You can hear whispering around you. You get sworn at, sometimes even spat at. Fights are frequent. Jewish shops are set on fire. Occasionally there are actually minor riots. Provoked by what I refer to as 'scum.'[336]

What's worse: slanderous stories have been circulating about us Jews. They say we worship a donkey's head as our God and have such a head in our Temple.[337] Supposedly we hate all Greeks and are fattening them up to sacrifice them to God in our Temple.[338] We weren't liberated from Egypt with God's help but driven out because we were carrying serious sickness."[339]

"Are such absurd accusations really taken seriously, Levi?"

"For much of the ordinary population, I'm afraid so.[340] I think more sophisticated people take them with a grain of salt, but I'm not certain. Maybe they feel too 'civilized' to embrace such slander openly.

I should add something, though, Amos. Such animosity to-wards our people isn't general. There are also those among the Greeks who have a high regard for our way of life and show deep respect for a unique, moral God. They're referred to as the 'God-fearing' and often come to our synagogues. But they're not real Jews. They don't get themselves circumcised and they often don't keep to the dietary laws.[341] Incidentally: the number of Jews in Alexandria may be overestimated because they include these people."

"Do they try and improve attitudes towards us, the Jews?"

"Not that I've noticed."

"Those are the facts, Levi. What interests me far more is how you, yourself, feel. Are you happy here?"

Levi gave me a surprised look.

"You find that question too personal," I said, quickly.

"No, not at all, but, to be honest I hadn't expected it. I would want to put that question another way: Am I content here? Happiness is momentary, a flash or, at most, an extended flash. Contentment is an ongoing feeling, at least as long as circumstances don't change drastically.

So, am I content here, you ask? Up to a point. I'm content with my work, what I earn, with my synagogue, with the community I'm part of, with the cultural life around me: the public speakers, the beauty of Greek architecture, the poetry, dramas, statues; beauty that, in a manner of speaking, is within hand's reach."

"Would you call yourself a Hellenized Jew?"

"I don't like that term." He paused for a moment and then, in a slightly irritated and decided tone, he continued, "I'm no renegade, no turncoat. I am, above all, a Jew, but not a Jew who has wrapped himself in a cocoon. I've moved with the times and acknowledged the Hellenistic revolution. That doesn't make you a bad Jew. If there's anyone who embodies that view, then it's Philo."

"So could I say that you have it both ways?"

"Yes, you certainly can and, to be honest, I like having it both ways!"

"You said you were content up to a point. So what's lacking?"

"You must know that, Amos. What's lacking is a feeling of certainty, of safety. Tensions – and there are always tensions – can get out of hand, ending up in large-scale violence. I'm not sure the Roman authorities won't put a stop to the privileges we've acquired at some point. They needed us to begin with. At the time, the Romans weren't welcomed here with open arms. So they tried to get us on their side. In the meantime, though, the Roman Empire has become supreme. They don't have to soft soap anyone any longer and they just about tolerate us here."

"My I ask you one last question?"

"I can't imagine it's going to be the last, from what I've seen of you so far, but it will be at least for today, I assure you. After answering it, I'm off to bed."

"Looking back, wouldn't you rather have stayed in Judea?"

"Again, I can only give you an indecisive answer: yes and no.

Yes, because I'll never feel fully accepted here. I'm a resident, not a citizen. I don't really feel at home here.

No, because then I would have missed out on the rich spiritual life of this city. Besides which, not everything in the garden has been rosy in Judea, either. Not during the reign of our Hasmonean monarchs, not under King Herod and not under the current Roman regime. There are plenty of Hellenized heathens who don't like us in Judea, too. Balaam divined that we would be a people who 'live apart and don't consider themselves one of the nations.'"[342]

"That's really rather pessimistic, Levi. I focus on Isaiah's prediction that there will be a day when many peoples will come and say, 'Come, let us go up to the mountain of the Lord, to the Temple of the God of Jacob. . . . The law will go out from Zion, the word of the Lord from Jerusalem.'[343] That statement gives me hope."

"Hope of what, Amos?"

"Hope that mutual respect will win out over mutual animosity. But now you, too, should stop asking questions."

Levi began to laugh. "Rascal."

"So may I conclude that you feel it's possible to be an emancipated, but still authentic Jew?"

"Absolutely, Amos!"

"That statement gives me the hope that things will work out for me in the future. Good night then."

"Have you got another appointment with Philo?"

"Yes, tomorrow evening."

"Well, as I said, you're a privileged person, Amos. Sleep well."

D.   AN EXECUTIVE ENTITY?

The next evening, I went to meet Philo feeling far calmer. He'd put me at my ease. When I arrived, he leaned back in his chair, looked past me and, without further ado, continued our discussion of the previous evening, as if there had been no interruption.

"Can an immaterial, transcendental God, devoid of human attributes, bring forth a concrete world?"[344] It was as if he were talking to himself. "The immaterial can't bring forth matter. It's simply not possible. Any more than beauty can bring forth beauty. It needs an intermediary: man."

"How do you see the Lord's role in the creation process?"

"I just said that the Lord has no human attributes. Well, that's not entirely right; He does have one: reason, the ability to think; He *is* reason, pure reason, the ultimate reason, the zenith of what can be achieved with reason. The Lord had ideas. In our case, ideas about a concrete world, about creating man. He wasn't able to materialize His ideas, though. He was lacking the tools, as it were. He's a super architect, but needs an executive entity to put his plans into practice."[345]

"So you see the Lord as a pure theoretician, a thinker, a kind of super philosopher."

"Yes, I do. That means he has to have an executive, an entity that executes His ideas. I've called that entity Logos, a term I borrowed from the Greek thinkers, the Stoics in particular. They defined it as a primeval force that brought forth the universe, manages it and allows it to continue existing; a kind of superb elixir of life. They also refer to the Logos as nature and the soul of the universe.

I've adopted this concept and given it another meaning. To my way of thinking, the Logos is the earthly-oriented aspect of the Lord, an attribute shall we say, which enables Him to act practically."

"God's executive arm, you mean."

"That's right. It's also that aspect of Him that maintains contact between Him and us people."

"Could it also be that the Lord has various forms?"

"There are Greek thinkers who claim that. The world as it has been created is certainly no paradise, they say, it also has its objectionable sides. The Creator isn't a craftsman, let alone an incompetent one. He evidently left his creative work to a lesser deity: Plato calls this the *demiurge*. Some even feel this is what is responsible for the evil in the world.

The idea of an intermediary power between Creator and creation seems likely to me. And the idea of the task being put in the hands of a second God – an inferior one at that, possibly even an evil genius – I reject that categorically."

"Your reasoning amazes me, Philo. You're a Jew, you believe in the uniqueness and indivisibility of the Lord.[346] So how can you reconcile that conviction with the idea of a Logos?"

"Okay, I'm interpreting your question as: 'What is the Logos' status?' That question is, indeed, cardinal. It plays on my mind, too. Is the Logos part of the Lord; is it a tool used by the Lord, or is it an entity operating with a certain degree of independence? I've termed the Logos 'God's first-born son'[347] and branded him a lieutenant of the 'great King.'[348] Are those the designated terms? I'm not sure."

"They suggest a kind of beautified *demiurge*."

Philo ignored my remark.

"I haven't made up my mind, Amos. I'll never make it up.[349] Philosophers can't prove anything; at best they can make things plausible. To me, the introduction of the idea of the Logos in thinking about God's way of working is plausible. What's more, it provides an extra bonus. Our Hellenized compatriots are familiar with the concept. This makes our Torah more accessible and acceptable to the more sophisticated amongst them."

I was fidgeting uneasily on my chair. Philo noticed. "Well, out with it. Say what you've got to say. Never shy away from discussion."

"To be truthful, Philo, I don't find that Logos idea plausible."

"What are your arguments? I don't begrudge anyone a plausible thought." His tone was decisive.

"I feel more at home with the idea that I was taught as normative, Philo."

"Norms can be erroneous and therefore treacherous, Amos."

I went on, unperturbed. "The way I see it, the Lord has two countenances: one facing up to heaven and one facing down to the Earth. He's both transcendental and immanent; that's what I was taught. These are His priorities, not those of two distinguishable beings. He resides in a divine realm but, at the same time, His spirit – the *Shechina* (Hebrew) was hovering over the earth during the creation.[350] That is still the case and that will always be the case. That's what I assume. Otherwise, why did we build a Temple, Philo? Surely not for an inaccessible, transcendental God, nor for a divine appendix, which you refer to as the Logos."

Philo laughed approvingly. "You're making it difficult for me, boy. You claim that your view is a normative one. That may be so for Jerusalem, but my criteria are different. In my view, an abstraction – in other words the Lord – can't be understood in the concrete – in other words, the world. To put it another way: the beginning – that is the creation idea – and the end –the act of creation – may well be linked, but one can't be deduced from the other."

"I'm not a knowledgeable man, nor a thinker like you, Philo, but . . ."

He stopped me. "Don't try to imply that you feel so insignificant. It's not true. You are and you feel like a thinker, a budding thinker at least."

"No, I don't feel like a thinker, Philo, not even a budding one. I do ponder though . . . But, to finish my sentence, our Almighty can do anything; that's what almighty means. He *is* the beginning and the end. And, more realistically, why shouldn't the Lord be able to change his line of vision, even his form? After all, people can. He must be able to adapt to changing circumstances."

"People, yes, but I can't see the Lord as a spiritual chameleon. He is both eternal and constant."

"And, with all due respect, Philo, I can't see why the Designer couldn't and, in this case, shouldn't also be the executor. You say the executor only does what it's told to do. But that's not so. Executors can be hard-headed, sometimes going their own way, especially when they notice the Designer isn't or is no longer interested in the project. Apart from which, they're sometimes forced to adapt the design, when circumstances change, for example."

"Now, there you've hit the nail on the head: God's design for the world was perfect whereas the result, to put it mildly, is not. The Lord can't be responsible for that; it has to be down to the executor. Don't get me wrong, though, Amos. I certainly don't see the Logos as a god or an idol. God's alter ego is perhaps a better image. After all, you don't see the *Shechina* as an idol, either, do you?"

"No, of course not, but not as a creative entity, either."

"You're a good debater, young man, but a typical product of a Pharisee school. Let's just say that, on this point, we've reached a draw in our game of chess."

"That makes me proud. Tying with a master, but . . ."

"Ah, another 'but', Amos."

"I'm afraid so, Philo; I'm not yet ready to concede a draw. I still have a couple of moves in store."

"Go ahead, then."

"You presented a pragmatic argument when defending the Logos concept, aimed at making our Lord more acceptable for Hellenized fellow citizens. Isn't that, in a manner of speaking, a slap in the face for Him?"

"Certainly not. Belief in the Lord can't be seen separately from politics. We notice that here every day."

"So do we Jews have to justify our lives to the outside world? Isn't that far beneath our dignity?"

"No, the feeling of dignity is nice, but feeling accepted and respected is even nicer."

"I don't see it like that, Philo. I don't want to justify myself. I'm proud of my God and my people. Let the skeptics justify their skepticism!"

"Heroically spoken, Amos, but if you ever end up in the diaspora, you'll soon change your tune."

There was a silence. Philo shuffled a couple of sheets of writing that were spread over his table. A pointless act in the given situation.

"Have I offended you?"

"No, Amos, a philosopher who can't take criticism isn't very wise. Your words did hit me hard, though. I've got to go now. We can continue this conversation the day after tomorrow. Until then."

With one of the foliants under his arm he walked out of the room.

E.   THE WORD

A few days later, Philo greeted me as if nothing had happened. I started in straight away. "I've been thinking about what you said."

"Not a bad idea, Amos. You still don't accept a draw?"

"Not yet, Philo. You assume the Creator has an executive intermediary. Is that idea actually new? Doesn't it come close to what's written in Genesis, namely that the Lord created using the words: 'Let there be' He said, and there it was. I think that's a lovely image: The creative word. Man was also given the word, evidently as a creative tool. Doesn't that 'creative word' come close to what you mean by the Logos?"

"Close, yes."

"So why don't I come across the concept of the Logos in Moses' scriptures?"

"Because 'close to' isn't the same as 'congruent with.' Designer and executor can be separated; an idea and its verbalization can't. We can distinguish between them but not separate them."

"A good thing too, Philo; the idea of not having any authority over the words I express my thoughts with doesn't bear thinking about."

I thought Philo was beginning to look impatient. "May I go on?"

"Yes, you may, young man, you're annoying me but, at the same time, you're amusing me. I love manifest intelligence."

"We get to know the Lord through his word, the Torah, don't we?"

"I won't deny that."

"In that case, who am I getting to know, Philo? The Lord or the Logos?"

"In the first instance God's Logos, but behind that hangs the Creator's world of ideas, like an indispensable backdrop."

"That idea doesn't appeal to me, Philo. In the Torah, I'm seeking the Lord himself, not some semiautonomous divine derivate. For me, as a Jew, the Lord is unique, one and indivisible.[351] I don't need the concept of the Logos. For me, it adds nothing desirable to the concept of God; it detracts from it!"

"Don't be so emphatic, young man. Don't forget the Lord Himself made a distinction between Creator and creation. Is it not written that the Lord laid the work of creation in the hands of Wisdom: 'The Lord possessed me at the beginning of His way,' says Wisdom, 'before His works of old.' And Wisdom 'was daily His delight, rejoicing always before Him.'[352]

Logos, as you know, is the Greek word for reason. The notions of wisdom and reason are virtually the same. Reason is the source of wisdom. Wisdom was God's creative hand. He says so Himself. I'm not making it up."

"I don't agree with you, Philo. First of all, according to my teachers, the words you're quoting are probably from the hand of King Solomon. I wonder if they represent God's view or the king's.

Secondly, like the word, wisdom can't be divorced from the one who produces and reveals that wisdom. The wise man, his wisdom and his word are inextricably linked."

Philo's right foot began to jiggle rapidly. "Okay, you stick to Jerusalem's traditional interpretation and I'll stick to mine, let's say the Alexandrian interpretation. Let that be so. I offer you that draw again."

"This time, I accept your offer, again proudly, but I still have a couple of questions concerning this game. I hope they won't offend you. May I?"

He didn't answer, but got up. "I have to go out for a while, but I'll be back soon."

Soon was not quite as soon as it implied.

F.   ASSIMILATION OR EMANCIPATION?

When Philo came back, he remained standing at the table. "I'm not so easily offended by genuine critical interest, Amos. Go ahead."

"Don't you think you're rather Hellenized in your thinking, Philo? Perhaps too Hellenized? Aren't you mixing too much Greek water with the Jewish wine?"

"What the Greeks serve is wine, too, a different wine, not water. Yes, Amos, I'm Jewish *and* Greek. I might almost add: may I?"

His words sounded defensive. He evidently felt he was being attacked.

"The Greek way of thinking fascinates me. In any case, it's hard for me to get away from it. I live in an entirely Hellenized city; Greek is my first language. I was educated at a Greek school, where they teach not only sport, as they seem to think in Jerusalem, but all kinds of other aspects of Greek culture, subjects such as literature, rhetoric, philosophy and logic. Mathematics and astronomy are also highly prized. At the theatre, I was introduced to Greek drama. Breathtaking! I saw magnificent statues in their temples. I go to chariot races, boxing matches and other sporting events. I'm a Hellenized Jew and I'm not ashamed to admit it. But I am a Jew, one who is proud of his people, proud of his heritage. I'm proud of the Torah, a work that already encapsulates everything that Greek philosophy has touched on."

What a brazen claim, I thought, the Torah being the foundation of Greek philosophy. But I saved that topic for later. I decided to provoke him the same way I'd Levi.

"No response, Amos?"

"I was just thinking, Philo. So you like and have it both ways."

"Yes, but I would put it a more civilized way: I keep both eyes open. You get a better perspective when you look with two eyes than you do with one."

"Isn't that a sophisticated synonym for assimilation?"

"I'm talking about emancipation, Amos, adapting to a new situation by adopting, assimilating certain elements."

"Based on clearly-understood self-interest?"

"Based on genuine interest and self-interest. Here, we listen to common sense. A hundred thousand Jews live in this city and they've been here for a very long time. Nevertheless, we're seen as outsiders and I'm no exception. I'm known here as Philo Judaeus – Philo the Jew – not Philo the Alexandrian. That speaks volumes, doesn't it? The Hellenized population has little sympathy for Jews. To survive, in fact to retain our Jewish identity, we have to adapt. A strange paradox for you, a Jerusalemite, perhaps, but it's easy for you to talk!"

"Wouldn't it be more accurate to say compromising than adapting?"

"Well, in my view the concepts are virtually identical. Adaptation is impossible without compromises."

"I'm wondering whether those compromises come from both sides."

"No, Amos, just yours truly, us Jews. That goes without saying. We've Hellenized, albeit to differing degrees. The other party didn't become more Jewish. We accept that situation. There isn't any other choice."

"But there was another choice, Philo: to live and continue living in a country with a dominant Jewish culture."

Philo looked at me resignedly. I saw no sign of irritation. "You're lecturing me, young man. You're a seasoned smart Alec, but you're not stupid. That makes up for it. Yes, my family left Judea. Yes, out of self-interest. Judea didn't offer enough opportunities. The Mediterranean area was Hellenizing and flourishing. Alexandria was becoming a centre of trade, culture and science. I've been able to fully blossom here, without feeling the hot breath of 'Jerusalem,' often so orthodox and narrow-minded, breathing down my neck. Without blowing my own trumpet, I feel I'm doing a service to Jewish culture with my work."

"What do you mean, Philo?"

"I mean I endeavour to make it clear that our teachings are not tribal, but universal and that, as I said, the ideas of the Greek philosophers are already encapsulated within them and Moses can therefore be seen as the greatest philosopher of all time."[353]

"That's quite a statement. Can you prove it?"

"I try to, with in-depth analysis of the sacred texts; by discovering the meaning lying concealed behind the literal text."

"But, surely, that's what legal scholars in Jerusalem try to do, as well?"

"Yes, but they don't go anything like far enough. In my opinion, many of these texts are meant purely symbolically. I'm attempting to find out what the Lord actually wanted to communicate."

"Would the Lord really have hidden his meaning so thoroughly? Only made it accessible for those who feel they have a monopoly on wisdom?"

"Your irony is inappropriate, Amos, but my answer is: He does. I'll tell you more about allegorical interpretation some other time.[354]

Now, let me come back to your question about my double loyalty. Incidentally, the question is also bordering on the inappropriate. No one here dares speak to me like that. Anyway. Yes I have a double loyalty. Yes, I know that term isn't looked on favorably in Jerusalem. Unjustifiably. Human intellect isn't a polished pebble; it's a cut diamond. The more facets it has, the more finely it's cut, the more the stone sparkles. The more loyalties the human intellect has, the richer its existence. With me, the Jewish and Greek loyalties fought for precedence. It ended in a draw. Harmonization of the two; that's what my life's been about."

"Choices have to be made, nonetheless, Philo."

"Not too quickly, young man, and certainly not at your age. You mustn't rein in your intellect. Philosophize. Keep philosophizing your whole life through. Try as many flavors as possible. Don't be afraid of combining flavors. But that's enough imagery for now. If you go for on too long you get bogged down."

"May I continue without imagery for a moment?"

Philo nodded.

"You're boasting about Greco-Roman culture, but what do you think about those naked sports, that veneration of the body – you who are so fond of the intellect – of the gladiator fights in which people, often slaves, have to fight against wild beasts, 'games' that seem to amuse the masses. What do you think of the bacchanals and sexual excesses with which Levi tells me the so-called god Dionysus is 'honored'? Isn't that decadent, to put it mildly? Isn't all that contrary to the standards the Lord gave us?"

"I quite agree with you. I've cherry picked from Greek culture, leaving the rest for what it is: barbarism. I do find it incomprehensible that a civilization that produced Plato, Homer and Euripides should take delight in such excesses. And not just the proletarians; a great many of the intelligentsia, too. As I said, I don't exclude myself. I do attend some events.[355] Am I ashamed of that? Well, in the presence of the moral purist you seem to be, yes, I am a little."

He is right, you know, I thought. Don't start moralizing. Watch out for hypocrisy.

"Do you try and discourage those excesses? After all, you have got some influence."

"Not much with our hosts. They'd have my head and it might even lead to persecutions. I try and impress on Jews that intellect is our crown jewel and the body it's rather ordinary carrier. That's a core theme for me. But I'll come back to it.[356] Where that's concerned, I leave the Greeks alone. I aim for peaceful coexistence. Not confrontation."

"That's understandable Philo, but I don't envy you your position in this. Just one more question about your Greek sympathies, if you'll allow me."

Philo nodded.

"You were telling me that Greek philosophers interpret the creator as a supernatural being that creates but doesn't care about its creation. How can you reconcile that with the idea of an Olympus, a place where a whole lot of gods are supposed to live, each with their own mandate? Beings that are often as unpredictable and uncontrolled in their behavior as we humans are. Not exactly a very good example for us!"

"I find that difficult to understand, too. The only thing I can imagine is that the image of a distanced 'origin of all origins' appeals to intellectuals and the idea of Olympus appeals more to ordinary people. The population here recognizes those gods; they can identify with them. What's more, the statues they make of them and the temples in which they're worshipped are often grand and imposing. Most proletarians' lives are lived at a physical and sensorial level. Their mental development lags behind."

"Don't be so elitist, Philo: an intellectual, aristocratic upper crust – philosophically oriented – and, far below, plebeians who don't see and never will see the light above.[357]

"Haven't *yet* seen, Amos. Plato is quite clear about that in his work *Politeia*. The administration of the community must never be put into the hands of the uneducated masses for whom truth is the great unknown. The opposite also applies, though. The educated mustn't negate their responsibility to pass on their knowledge. He was right."

"Now we've introduced inequality, Philo. I assume the Lord

imagined it otherwise. He didn't create a stratified society. He called for mutual respect."[358]

"You're touching on a raw nerve there, but don't forget that the remedy requires two-way traffic. I mean the lower stratum must feel the need to climb upwards and the upper stratum must be prepared to descend and help them. That's a long-term project, Amos, I can tell you. Be realistic."

"I'm too young for that, Philo."

"Well, that's a good place to stop. It's getting late. I'm going to bed. I'd like to invite you to come tomorrow evening. You've caught my interest. Good night."

G. REAL OR UNREAL WORLD?

Philo greeted me with the words, "Welcome, my boy." He hadn't spoken to me like that before. There was a carafe of water on the table and, for the first time, a plate of biscuits. I was feeling more and more at ease, even a little honored.

"I'm curious to see what you've got planned for this evening," Philo continued. Getting straight down to business was evidently his style. No wasting time with small talk.

"Yesterday, when we were talking about the Lord, you said that he created the world on the basis of ideas. I don't really understand that. Ideas are something typically human. Man is the only one who engages in ideas. Dogs don't have them, or trees; at least as far as we know. So aren't you humanizing the Lord and contradicting yourself?"

"I'm not humanizing the Lord. On the contrary. You misunderstand me. I use the word idea in the sense given to it by Plato, in particular. In *Politeia*, which I already mentioned, and also in another work, *Timaeus*, he refers to the concept of Idea with a capital letter. Do you know anything about this?"

"I'm afraid I have to say little or nothing."

"I'll try and explain it you simply. Back then, Plato founded an academy in Athens. He and his students were primarily concerned with the distinction between the material, the senso-rial, discernible world and the spiritual world. Plato's vision was expressly dualistic. His opinion was that the distance between the two is close to infinite. An opinion I share. Plato went fur-ther, stating that the world as we perceive it with our senses, the material world, is no more than a vague echo of the actual world, an imperfect copy. Worse still, he claimed that sensorial impressions would obstruct the view of the real world."

"I don't understand, Philo. What do you mean by the 'real world'? The spiritual world?"

"You can see it like that."

"I see the spiritual world as the world of the intellect, that compartment of our being that houses our power of thought, our reason and our power of imagination."

"Absolutely."

"That is, indeed, a different world from the one we perceive, but isn't that akin to kicking down an open door? Apart from which, as far as I'm concerned the material and spiritual worlds are not so far apart. They intersect, overlap, and that's not all. Both are mine, both make me who and what I am. To me, the material world is just as 'real' as the spiritual world.

And why, Philo, does Plato talk so condescendingly about the world we perceive, in which we live, our material world? It never ceases to fascinate me. And that world is supposed to be 'a poor copy of the real world'? Where did he get that idea?"

I was starting to get wound up.

Philo touched my hand. "Easy now, my boy. He's not deni-grating the world we live in so much as the world as we perceive it. He feels our observations are unreliable and deceptive."

"But those senses are the only receivers for the outside world. What should we trust, then?"

"We need to trust in reason, my boy. I'll explain it to you with the parable Plato himself used, but from the mouth of an interlocutor, his fellow philosopher Socrates. Imagine, he says, that you're in a dark cave, chained up. Behind you, a fire is burning. It's the only source of light in the cave. People are walking between you and the fire, holding all kinds of things in the air. You can see their shadows on the wall in front of you, but not the things themselves. What you see are vague reflections, in ever-changing forms. It's the same with the world we perceive. It's no more than a vague shadow of the real world."

"It's a nice story, Philo, but what's that got to do with the way we live? Are we supposed to be chained up in a poorly-lit cave? It seems to me that the opposite is true. We're free people, able to look around ourselves in all directions in a well-lit world. We can compare our impressions with other people's and come to a consensus. As long as we have our wits about us, we see the world clearly; originals, in my view, not shadows, not copies."

"You can't say that, Amos, as long as you don't know what the originals are."

"So what are the originals and where can I find them?"

"Well, Amos, Plato calls the originals, the basic forms, the archetypes of everything there is, you might say, Ideas, with a capital I. Of course I mean that symbolically. Where can you find those Ideas? Not on Earth, but above, in God's spirit."

"As far as I'm concerned, Philo, you're speaking a secret language; I don't understand a word of it. Surely, ideas don't constitute a separate world. Ideas with a lowercase I, that is. Thought constructions – and that's what ideas are, aren't they? – form in the heads of people and are dependent on those heads. Ideas don't have any autonomy. They're not entities that can exist by themselves, separate from man. The world of notions is part of *this* world."

"That's not what Plato understands by the term 'Idea' and I go along with him in this. He elevates the concept above the everyday level – the vulgar level – to the metaphysical sphere. He uses them to define, as I said, the basic form, the prototype of everything that exists in our world, both the things and the notions we formulate, such as beauty, goodness and righteousness.

It refers to their essence, to those aspects that are eternal and constant. Essences, perhaps that's the best equivalent."

"Hold on a moment Philo, if you don't mind. My head is spinning. Basic principles, essences, prototypes, you're using such difficult terms again. Please explain it to me!"

Philo got up and paced around the room. "I'll try. You have to realize, Amos, that you live in an unstable world. Everything changes. Rapidly – a fading flower, or slowly – a growing tree, or continuously: a river, for example. The direction of flow, the water flowing through it, the structure of the surface, they're forever changing. It seems there are no stable concepts: flower, tree, river. That can't be true. The Lord couldn't have created a world on that basis. The creation assumes stable building blocks."

"But, Philo, you're putting yourself in the Lord's shoes. We know nothing about how He works."

"True, but my conclusion is logical, inevitable. Without stable building material there is no construction. There have to be building blocks: a flower blueprint, a tree blueprint, a river blueprint, prototypes possessing the properties that apply to all flowers, all trees and all rivers. Plato called those prototypes Ideas, or Forms. I talked of essences just now. Archetypes is another equivalent. I prefer the term Idea.

What applies to things and natural phenomena also applies to concepts. Those, too, are far from stable. Take the concept of beauty, for example. What is considered beautiful varies from person to person, from community to community, from era to era. There has to be a stable concept of beauty, independent of time, place and human preference.

The same applies *mutatis mutandis* to concepts such as goodness and righteousness. People are unable to define them unambiguously. A basic concept, an Idea, must also exist for these.

Together, Ideas, of which there must be countless numbers, form the mold, the basis on which the world was created. They constitute the 'real world,' the world concealed behind the sensorial world!"

"Can mankind gain knowledge of that world?"

"To a certain degree, Amos. You can't interpret that literally. After all, the Idea world is at a metaphysical level. It's part of the divine realm. The only way to get there is by means of intellect, reason. Thinking, reflecting, philosophizing, exchanging ideas with other thinking people takes you in that direction. Step by step you advance. Some progress further and are able to catch a glimpse of that divine world. Some don't get very far and give up prematurely. No man can enter there. It's part of the Lord's private domain.[359] Moses may have been the only exception."[360]

I listened in fascination but also increasing amazement. "Where do these Ideas come from, Philo, who formulated them?"

"The Lord Himself, Amos, who else?"

"With the help of His executor, the Logos, I suppose?"

"I assume He didn't need it for this. His own reason would have been enough." He stopped for a moment, and laughed, "I see I've got a budding relativist here."

I was, indeed, feeling an increasing inclination to contradict him. I was tense.

"No, Philo, no. I'm not a skeptic; I just don't agree with you." I was shocked by my own comment. "You must think I'm an arrogant windbag, but . . ."

"Now I don't, Amos. A teacher is proud when his pupil becomes an outspoken opponent. To put it crudely, dialectics is power food for reason. Please, go on."

"He talked about the world of Ideas, the real world. For me, that's an unreal world. You're turning the Lord into some kind of intellectual bulwark. I haven't found anything in the Holy Scriptures that refers to that. Only a philosopher can think up something like that. It seems like philosophizing for philosophizing's sake. I only know one world: the one I live in, the world I perceive, that I experience. Above that is a superhuman world, the Lord's world. For man, it's not knowable, certainly not with the help of reason. No man can see Him and live, the Lord says so Himself.[361] I get to know Him in Moses' scriptures. I meet Him not through my senses, not through my reason, but by a third way, that of the imagination. I, myself, call that the 'unreal world.' Not because it doesn't exist, but because it exists only for me and has no general validity."[362]

"In one sense, you've understood me well, Amos. I do, indeed, interpret the Lord as an intellectual bulwark. His being is reason, pure reason. Reason generates wisdom. His Wisdom is the source of the Ideas. He draws from that wealth of Ideas when formulating the blueprints for the Creation. Consequently, I also call the Lord the 'Being,' the origin of everything there is.[363] In other words, the Lord's world and that of the Ideas more or less coincide."[364]

"How does our intellect compare with divine intellect, Philo?"

"That's a good question, Amos. Make no mistake. God's reason is not, as you suggested, a 'human attribute." It's the other way round. Human reason is a spark of His reason. A seed, you might say, from which a spiritual flower can grow. I emphasise the word 'can.'"

"A sound argument, Philo, but is it actually true? You speak with such certainty about God's way of working. I find that . . ." I considered for a moment. Philo looked at me, questioningly. "I find that . . ." I'd wanted to say "presumptuous." What I did say was, "Did the Lord give you permission?"

"No, little critic, I wasn't given carte blanche. I'm trying to imagine His way of working. Anyone has the right to his own idea.

Now, for a change, I'd like to reverse the roles and examine your claims. I heard you say you encounter the Lord in your perception, on private territory, in other words. That suggests He wouldn't exist outside of it. And that borders on disbelief. It's thoughts like those that challenge our belief, not those of the Greeks."

"I'm not suggesting the Lord doesn't exist. He exists for me, but I can't say any more than that. My certainty is purely subjective."

"That's the same as doubt and, in this case, that doubt is ungrounded. The Lord exists. As I said: no creation without a creator. That's not an axiom; it's a logical conclusion. His world is the real one. It's a product not of the power of imagination but of the power of thinking."

"My power of thinking is inadequate for this, Philo. So far, at least."

"Evidently I haven't been able to convince you, Amos, or you haven't wanted to listen. I'm going to leave it there. You're obviously indefatigable. I'm not."

"Not for good, I hope?"

"No, but for today. You can come back tomorrow evening if you like. Good night."

H. ESSENCES?

When I arrived the next evening, Philo greeted me heartily, but the words that followed sounded sarcastic. "What have you come to teach me today, Amos?"

"I haven't come to teach you anything; I'm learning from you. I've come to ask questions and you gave me the right to respond."

"I did. You've aroused my curiosity again, Amos."

"You assume that essences exist. That objects and concepts are based on a pre-existing, clearly-defined, durable design. I can imagine that applies to objects. Throughout the ages, a flower has remained recognizably a flower, regardless of the species. For concepts, that seems unlikely to me. I can't imagine there is a ready-made model for concepts such as beauty. There are far too many nuances to beauty. The beauty of a body is not comparable with that of a poem, a building, a sculpture, a landscape, a particular notion and so forth.

Neither can I imagine any stable, indestructible, timeless core for goodness and righteousness, the other two concepts you mentioned, no matter how hard philosophers seek it!"

Philo gave me an intense, though not unfriendly look. "I don't think you have a very high opinion of philosophers. You're not short of a certain cheekiness, either. I forgive you for that. I'm wondering if I should call you hard-headed or precocious.

In any event, I'm going to make a final move in this chess game. I consider it unlikely that chaos can be formed into a cosmos without stable, pre-existing building material. Even the Lord can't build something – and *what* a something! – out of nothing."[365]

"Believe me, Philo, I hold philosophers in extremely high regard. I hope to become one myself. Sometimes, though, I think they reach too high. May I make one last move in this chess game, too?"

Philo sighed. "Go on, then."

"Do you see the Ideas theory as a possibility, a hypothesis or a certainty?"

"I assume it. Such a notion seems plausible to me."

"So you have your doubts?"

"I'm not sure. Uncertainty characterizes the existence of the philosopher. I already told you that. If there were any certainties then philosophers would be superfluous."

"If uncertainty is the basis of your existence, Philo, then don't you have to accept that there are no highest common denominators for our concept apparatus, that the idea of an Idea is a mirage? That uncertainty is not just the basis for *your* existence; it *is* existence; that the quest for certainties is a dead-end street? I think that's worth examining, more than looking for possible fixed points in metaphysical space."

"I'm less hard-headed than you, Amos. I won't dismiss your points of view out of hand. They do, indeed seem worth studying. But no more than mine.

I'll leave it at that. Let's have your next question, or rather hypothesis."

I cleared my throat and frowned, feeling charged up, like before a match. Philo interpreted my facial expression correctly. "You want to make some kind of provocative statement and you're hesitant. Speak up, now; I can take it."

I. WORLDLY AND DIVINE SPIRITUALITY

I hesitated, but eventually came out with it. Rather emphatically, actually. "I find your views fundamentally un-Jewish."

Now it was Philo who frowned, evidently annoyed by my remark. "That accusation sounds serious. Certainly to the ears of someone who considers himself a pious Jew. Explain yourself," he replied in an almost imperative tone.

"As far as I understand, Jewish spirituality is worldly, rather than divine. [366] It's that paradox that makes that way of thinking so fascinating to me. A Jew worships the Lord in this world by making himself useful in some way to the community. Justice for all, regardless of their antecedents; care for the deprived, the lonely, the persecuted, respect for Creation and creations: that's what's asked of us.[367] It's in such affairs that the Jew encounters his Lord. Not in divine speculations."

Philo remained calm. "I don't deny that, Amos, but can you call that spirituality? For me, spirituality means being absorbed into and entering an immaterial, divine world."

"Not for Jews, Philo, at least not for this Jew. No esoteric high-flying. Rather, trying to give a spiritual dimension to the material world. That's what I call spirituality."

I stopped for a moment, thinking Philo would now react, but all he said was, "Go on, Amos."

"In my view, the Lord had a reason for revealing himself to us here on earth, on Mount Sinai, rather than from an inaccessible metaphysical space. What he seemed to be saying was, 'Here on earth is the meeting place for you and me. You will get to know

Me in My works here on Earth. I want to encounter you in your works here on Earth.' I believe a Jew is focused on the here and now, not on later in some hypothetical 'elsewhere.'"

Philo stroked his beard and still said nothing. I went on.

"Your call to use our reason to seek and keep seeking 'essences,' Ideas that are supposedly stored in the divine realm, is aimed in the opposite direction: vertically, not horizontally. That's what I call an un-Jewish attitude!"

Finally, Philo reacted. "Your comments are hurtful, Amos. I won't contradict you, but you're forgetting that a man can serve more than one interest. Your opinion isn't at odds with mine. Good, one of the core Ideas, calls us to act in your spirit. That doesn't rule out philosophizing. Take me. I philosophize for hours every day, seeking verticality, but I also make myself useful to our Jewish community, a horizontal activity. The latter sometimes even gets too much for me."[368]

"I've heard that, Philo, and the community is grateful to you. But not everyone is a Philo. What's more, that philosophizing evidently presents risks. Your reasoning is introducing alien motives into our spiritual foundation. They could overrun ours, jeopardizing the stability of the entire structure."

"Now I can hear the blinkered Judean talking again. I'll say it again: open both your eyes! What you describe as 'alien elements' are not stains, but a new, innovative component, an enrichment of our spiritual baggage."

"I can't see it like that, Philo. Your views are egocentric. It's all about 'me.' The 'me' seeks the metaphysical space; It wants to enrich itself spiritually, ultimately wants to be close to the Lord in the hope of gaining everlasting life for its soul. In your considerations, the 'other' hardly gets a look in."

"Again, the way I see it, it does. I do, indeed, serve myself, but I serve others as well. And that's my last word on the subject. I don't want to get into an argument about this," he concluded, irritated.

"I'm truly sorry if I'm doing you an injustice, but I don't want to do myself an injustice either by not speaking when I feel I must. May I pose just one more question?"

"Is it going to be a question or a point of view?"

"Well, it's a combination of the two, I'm afraid, Philo."

"You're not only courageous but bold, too, young man, but go ahead."

"I find the idea of the Idea dangerous!"

"To top it off! Un-Jewish *and* dangerous!"

"Yes, I do. Supposing essences existed, definitive and exhaustive definitions, then they would have to be generally accepted, axiomatically, as irrefutable truths. And supposing there were people who couldn't be convinced of those truths. What would happen to them? Would they be treated as apostates? Isn't there then a risk of intolerance? Wouldn't it lead to discrimination, to expulsion?"

"There is that chance. If you stubbornly deny the truth, then you're vulnerable. But don't worry, Amos. If, in the far-off future, the idea of the Idea inseminates the world, then the Idea of good will become dominant and come to the aid of these 'unbelievers' of yours. They can count on compassion."

"I hope doubt will remain on your side, Philo."

"I've never had a student who dared treat me as freely, almost as an equal. To be honest, I have to get used to it.

I'll see you again tomorrow evening." It sounded almost like an order.

J.   SORROW

I was feeling insecure again when I returned to Philo's room the next evening. I had been rather impertinent. Would he hold it against me?

Philo was sitting in an easy chair, rather than at the table. He got up and, with an inviting gesture, indicated a reclining chair. This was the first time. It reassured me.

"This time, for a change, I'm going to ask you a couple of questions, Amos. What do you do for a living?"

"My father's teaching me silversmithing. He gave me leave for this visit. He felt I could learn a lot from you and he was right."

"I'm glad to hear it. Are you married?"

"No, not yet."

"Isn't that unusual for a Jewish man of your age?"

"I often swim against the tide, Philo. I want to spread my wings. I don't want to be tied down with a family, yet."

"Okay; spread your wings wide and often, young man. But now over to you."

"If I understand correctly, then you see those who philosophize as the ideal type. Those who seek Ideas, the essence of things. Well, do we come into this world bereft of any inkling of what you call the Ideas world?"

"No, Amos, it's not like that. First, a little bit of philosophy – or perhaps, rather theology – borrowed from Plato and Moses. Man has a soul . . ."

"I'm well aware of that," I laughed.

Philo continued as if he had heard nothing. "That soul is enclosed in a material shell, the body."

"You already mentioned the prison house idea. It sounded strange to me. You were going to come back to it."

"I see you've been paying attention, Amos. Bear with me for a moment. Don't keep interrupting. The soul is, as I said, a divine gift, a spark of His Reason. It was created long before the body. In that pre-corporeal state, the soul resided in God's realm. At that time, it was still morally perfect and blessed with knowledge of the Ideas.[369]

At the time of the creation, the Lord decided to give the soul a temporary lodging in a material shell: our body.[370] The first man was still perfect in body and soul.[371] But things quickly went wrong. The first man was given company in the shape of a woman. Together, they discovered lust. Lust introduced desire, passion.[372] The soul lost some of its purity and its knowledge of the Ideas faded. Where the latter is concerned, once it's on Earth, from a practical point of view the soul has to start all over again."

"So the Lord's decision was a cardinal error?"

"Not an error, Amos, a mistake, less than accurate foresight. I suppose He assumed that, within the body, the soul would become more sophisticated, but the opposite was the case."

"You're suggesting that the body drags the soul down."[373]

"I'm not suggesting it, Amos; you can see it happening before your very eyes. Once it's contained in the body, the soul becomes beset with passions and urges, by the longing for pleasure, for the sensual, the material. These needs come from the body. They can't be lastingly satisfied, they eat away at the soul, eroding its ability to aim upwards and stay in touch with its land of origin, the divine world of Ideas. The soul, the home of reason, is beset by irrational needs and has to do its utmost to rein them in. That energy could have been better spent on building a way upwards."

"Do you mean to say that life without passions, focused entirely on philosophizing, is the ideal form of life?"

"Yes, I do. The Stoics call that a state of *apatheia*."

"You say the Lord miscalculated. Another possibility, Philo, is that He did it deliberately. The Lord was testing man. Would the soul be able to resist being assailed by those irrational urges once it was inside the body?"

"Well, that certainly can't be ruled out. I hadn't thought about that. The Lord commanded that 'all men and boys should be circumcised.'[374] Perhaps He was, indeed, saying: endeavour to control yourself. Cut out passions from your life, or at least hold them in check.[375]"

"So I suppose you feel a lot of people fail that test."

"Unfortunately, yes."

"With the exception of philosophers?"

"That's what *I* assume, Mister Sarcastic."

"And those who do manage to keep a check on their passions are rewarded?"

"Yes, I think so. After death, their soul will return to its origins, the world of Ideas."[376]

"What happens to those who fail, who don't manage to control their irrational needs?"

"I don't know. I think those souls will disappear, possibly incarcerated in a subterranean area."[377]

"A good thing, too. The Lord would have quite a problem with that."

"Spare me the inappropriate jokes, Amos!" Philo yawned. I'm yawning not from boredom, but because you're exhausting me. I feel as if I'm on trial."

I didn't respond, feeling slightly overwhelmed. What were these contrived theories he was trotting out? Where did he get them? Spiritual contortions to get our scriptures to harmonize with Greek philosophy. I'm none the wiser for it.

Philo does say that he considers our Teachings superior and that the Greek philosophers have borrowed their notions from the scriptures of Moses, but to hear him talk like this, he's touching his forelock, bowing his reason to his patrons. I didn't say anything. I didn't want to shamelessly confront him again. "Why the silence, Amos? Have you finished having your say?"

"No, Philo, I don't run out of words that quickly. I always try and give a response."

"You are, indeed, a master at that. Go on, then."

"You say the soul leaves the body when it dies. So is the soul immortal?"

"The uncontaminated soul, yes, I have little doubt about that."

"What do you think happens to what you consider to be that accursed material shell?"

"What a way to put it, boy! That's not usual in philosophical circles. Anyway, the body disappears, it literally rots away."

"Are you sure of that?"

"As sure as one can be. So not a full hundred percent. Then there would be no room left for doubt. Do I ever doubt it then? Not while I'm awake, but when I'm asleep I do. I had a dream, not so long ago, or maybe it's a story I heard somewhere. Whatever, the story was about a king who had a plantation where marvellous figs grew. He appointed two guards. One was lame, the other blind. The lame one said to the blind one, 'I can see some lovely figs hanging there. Put me on your shoulders, then I can pick them and we can eat them together. So they did. A little while later, the king came by and asked what had happened to the figs. The lame one answered, 'Have I got legs to stand on?' And the blind one said, 'Have I got eyes to see?' The king placed the lame guard on the blind guard and judged them both.

I've never been able to entirely shake that dream, or story. Who knows? Maybe all of mankind will be held accountable." Philo spoke hesitantly.

"To the Lord or to itself?" I asked.

"I don't know, Amos. You're getting on my nerves."

"So you haven't got your emotions, your irrational urges, completely under control, then."

"Not by a long chalk. I realize how difficult that is. *Apatheia* is an ideal. An inaccessible ideal for me, I'm afraid. You're enticing me into making confessions, Amos. I'm surprised at myself. I'm going to bed. Maybe I'm overtired. You can come back the day after tomorrow."

He left the room without another word.

K.   BEYOND PASSION?

Two days later, I was promptly back in Philo's room. He started in straight away, as usual. "I keep confronting you with ideas that are evidently strange to you, Amos. They come from the Greco-Roman world, but they have been through a Jewish sieve; my intellect."

"That's what you think, but I still see so little that's Jewish in your notions, Philo. The body has a poor reputation, as far as you're concerned. It generates longings, passions, and corrupts the soul, which is reaching for higher spheres. You put the body down. Unjustifiably. It's thanks to our bodies that we can experience the world around us. Those experiences are food for the soul. The body doesn't obstruct its development, it advances it.

And yes, you're allowed to enjoy worldly things, what you call the sensory. You can enjoy your food, being with your wife, the prosperity your work has brought you, nature all around us. The Lord didn't label all this as negative. On the contrary! He said to us, 'Choose life.'[378] Sanctify life, enjoy life, help others to enjoy it, and don't concentrate on death and its possible aftermath. He gave us a task: make something better of the world and enjoy the results. Your ideas are at odds with that. You glorify death, the time which, so you believe, the soul will regain its freedom. I call that idea un-Jewish."

"I agree with you, Amos, that focusing on the worldly, on the material, on the body, can generate a lot of good, but it can also generate far more bad things: hedonism, greed, lust, passion that keeps us from the way upwards."

"Certainly, but don't forget that setting your sights upwards can keep you from your worldly obligations."

"Then you're talking about false piety, young man."

"Exactly, but the phenomenon isn't uncommon. I've often seen it around me.

Well, anyway, I've got another point that I have difficulty placing within a Jewish context. You put reason on a pedestal. In my view, that pedestal reaches far too high, almost to heaven. You're derogatory about feelings. I haven't found any of that aversion in Moses' scriptures."

"You've got hold of the wrong end of the stick. I was talking about emotions and passions, not feelings."

"But passions and emotions are part and parcel of feelings, Philo."

"Yes, of course, but these are extremes, feelings that have burst at the seams."

"Every normal phenomenon has its extremes. That's no

reason to down it. I hold reason in high esteem, but also feelings, including extremes.

"I can't abide by the idea of having to lead a life with little or no feelings, emotions and passions. I can't imagine not being able to be happy, even delirious, about good news; not being able to get cross, even furious, if someone has behaved unjustly towards me; not being sad, even distraught, at a major loss. My life would be dull and colorless."

"I understand that but, again, don't forget that emotions and passions can ruin life, especially life after death."[379]

"That may be so, Philo, but then reason can always intervene. You sort out the rotten apples and remove them, but you never throw away the entire store of apples! Without feelings, life is covered with a dingy film. Reason produces light, that's true, but not color."

"Intellect elucidates, Amos, and that's what it's all about. Colors distract from the essence. It's reason that enriches our existence."

"In my eyes, white light only illuminates half of reality or, to put it a better way: half of my reality. Anyway, as I said, I wanted to put another point to you. May I, or am I annoying you?"

"You don't let up and you don't get put off. It does you credit. Go ahead."

"I think you're trying to mask your impatience with a compliment, but I'm going to plough ahead. When I hear you talk like this, it seems to me you only view passions from the negative side, but there are such wonderful passions. In my view, you yourself are possessed by at least one passion: studying and philosophizing, a need that can't be satisfied for long. I know people who are passionate about helping others. I love my father and mother passionately. I'm very grateful for that. Rein in destructive passions and give constructive passions free rein, I would say."

"The line between the two is hard to draw in practice, Amos. What I would say is: keep away from fire to avoid getting burnt.

Temperance; total tranquillity to allow yourself to concentrate unimpeded on spiritualization. The Lord Himself is a shining example. He represents the ultimate *apatheia* and Moses came close."[380]

"Where did you get that from, Philo? The Lord is an impassioned Being? To put it irreverently, He seems to me to be a barrel of emotions. As a father, He is compassionate with our people. Our people don't consist of angels. That constantly evokes emotions in Him.

And Moses, then? Was he supposed to be beyond passion? Quite the opposite is true. In any case, that would have been a logical impossibility. How could he have led our recalcitrant people for forty years without passions, without regularly getting furious, yes even desperate?"[381]

"I've already told you, Amos, that's an illusion. It was written down that way to make the Lord a recognizable Being and Moses a recognizable person."

"I really can't accept that, Philo. I think you're painting our God and our greatest prophet to suit your own conviction."

I could feel myself getting worked up again. "I think you're talking about the Greek god, the creator without any interest in his creation, not about the Jewish God, the God we call Father. In my opinion you're turning Moses into a super Stoic. To make him acceptable to the Hellenized world, I suppose. Moses was one of us. An emotional person. You have no right to take away his Jewishness."

Philo began drumming his fingers impatiently on the table in front of him. I realized I'd gone too far and decided to back down.

"I'd like to come back for a moment to the discussion on the relationship between feelings and intellect, Philo. Feelings can run to excess, you stressed that, but so can the intellectual life. I'm talking about rulers who claim to have divine antecedents and treat their subjects like dirt. I'm thinking of intellect being used for unfair practices. Defamation used to eliminate rivals. I could go on. All I'm saying is that people can misuse any ability."

"Agreed, but that doesn't apply to philosophers. They seek the truth and aren't so easily tempted to misuse their intellect."

"But most people have their feelings pretty much in hand, Philo, not just philosophers."

"More buts, Amos. You'll wear the word out. Can't you ever concede? No, I don't share your optimism. The intellect is fairly resistant to excesses, but feelings are far less so. They can be stoked."

"I have one final question, Philo. You make such a clear distinction between intellect and feelings. Is that really possible, practicably speaking?"

Philo leaned back in his chair. "I'm listening. You're asking a question but I suspect you already have the answer ready!"

"You're right. In my view, it's impossible; there's a continuous interaction. I'll give you a personal example. I was really happy at the idea of travelling to meet you. I can attribute my feeling upset over the past few days to the fact that, in the near future, I won't be seeing you again. I can't separate those feelings from those thoughts."

Philo laughed. "Flatterer! Believe me, it's possible. Feelings, particularly feelings generated by physical needs, can be suppressed. It's a learning process. It's difficult to begin with. They keep rearing their heads, but they eventually fade. It demands concentration, a concerted intellectual effort. The stream of thoughts ultimately stems the rising feeling."

That, Master, is only theory, I thought. Do you really think a young man can successfully and permanently suppress his sex drive by using intellect? By enhancing his spirituality? Theoretical words from an elderly man! For decency's sake, I kept that thought to myself.

"Don't underestimate the driving force of reason," Philo continued.

"And don't underestimate the power of passion, either, if I may be so bold, Philo."

"I'll take your advice to heart, Amos. Let's close the discussion for today. Get yourself a good night's sleep."

L.   RETREAT

The next evening began in silence. Philo said nothing and I said nothing.

"You're very quiet, Amos," laughed Philo, "That normally doesn't bode well for me. I suspect there's another painful question or comment coming."

"A personal question, actually, Philo."

"As if your questions haven't been personal so far, but you're irresistible. I'm listening."

"You plead for an ascetic existence, from which the passions have ebbed, but isn't that just theory? You actually live a rich life here, not just spiritually; materially, too."

Philo looked pensive. After a while, he responded.

"No, I'm not a very good example of my philosophical views. My spirit is weak, despite all my good intentions. People often don't practice what they preach. For some, the pretence is even an attitude to life. It helps maintain their self-respect."

"That's not the way I meant it, Philo. I've got a tremendous amount of respect for you, even if I don't agree with many of your opinions."

"But I did mean it that way, Amos. You've wormed your way into my conscience. Sometimes I realize what you have so bluntly been saying. Then I feel moved to withdraw from this excessive life, to break away from the 'better circles,' this self-satisfied society.[382] I go to the Therapeutae, a group of extremely pious Jews, most of whom have settled in the desert some two hours to the west of the city, near the Mareotic Lake.[383] This group leads a truly ascetic life, renouncing personal possessions, living in poverty and aspiring to full sexual abstinence. The men devote themselves to studying the Holy Scriptures. I admire them. These men really 'live in the soul alone.' They are citizens of heaven and of the world. The Creator loves them.'[384] I find my bearings again when I'm with them. But after a little while I feel the pull of the city again, an irresistible urge. I act as if there's a task awaiting me there, but I'm just kidding myself."[385]

"That's not it, Philo. You're indispensable. That's what I've been told."

"I'm not indispensable, Amos. There are other leaders. I wish I'd had the strength of an Abraham. He fled the base and polluted prison house of the body to the world where the incorporeal and the imperishable dwell."[386]

"That's some interpretation, Philo. I'd like you to explain it to me at some point, but first I've got another question about the Therapeutae. I've never heard of them before. Their way of living is reminiscent of the Qumran community, which I've visited myself."

"I haven't, but I've heard of them. They, too, practice what I only preach. They're fully-fledged ascetics and I admire them for that."[387]

"I don't admire them, Philo. They've withdrawn from our society out of revulsion. Do they make any attempt to rectify whatever it is that revolts them? No! They just kick against it, convinced that they and they alone have a monopoly on divine wisdom. What an arrogant lot!"

"I know little or nothing of their views. But that does sound self-righteous. That's not the road to virtue, the way to what I allegorically call 'paradise.'"[388]

"You call them self-righteous. Don't those who feel they've got close to the world of the Ideas risk become self-righteous, too?"

"No, Amos, those are the people who really do possess a great deal of wisdom. Well, now I've have had my bellyful, young man."

"Of me, Philo?"

"Of your continual opposition."

"Enough for this evening?"

"Yes, you're still welcome but I would like to say one thing before you go. You've made it abundantly clear that you don't agree with me. You feel I'm too influenced by Greek thinking. You don't think there's anything to be gained with the concept of the Logos; the ideal of the *apatheia* is un-Jewish; an aversion to the body doesn't seem Jewish to you; you consider the Idea philosophy too far-fetched and so forth. You think I kowtow to what you call my patrons."

"I'm sorry if I've made you cross."

"I'm not cross, Amos. There's nothing wrong with criticism. I encourage it, even. You're partly right and partly wrong. Yes, I get a lot of my ideas from the culture I live in. But is that kowtowing? No, it's a slight nod, at most. I find those ideas stimulating. They complement our Teachings, refresh them, so they're valuable."

"But what's their added value?"

"They show us that our Teachings are not just a tribal affair, rules that are only valid for the Jewish community; no, they incorporate universal values. In other words, I want to show that Moses is the greatest lawgiver of all time and that his rules are for human society as a whole. I'm not corrupting our Teachings; I'm refining them."[389]

"I really can't agree with you, Philo. If you were to embellish a Greek temple with what are, in themselves, lovely Egyptian frescoes, then it would no longer be a real Greek temple; it would be a corruption."

"Not a corruption; an attempt – however crude – at reaching out.

In any event, there's another reason I feel at home with some Greek thinkers. There are those passages in Moses' scriptures that I dislike, where the Lord calls for entire nations to be wiped out, for example, women and children included. Surely that can't have been meant literally. There must be another concealed message. I try and divine it. That's what the Stoics did with Homer's writings, such as the Iliad. They were highly esteemed, seen as divine imprimatur, but, at first sight, the *dramatis personae* in those works often behave improperly. Stoics sought another meaning, the true meaning, and discerned wise, timeless lessons in those contested passages. I've adopted that method, known as allegorical interpretation, in my attempt to find the true, universal meaning of those divine texts. This has given inhuman passages a more human countenance. I'll come back to that. [See section *m* in this chapter]

But I digress. What I actually wanted to say was this: Don't be too apposite, Amos. Moderate your judgement. And I'm talking about moderation, not mediocrity. Wherever possible, choose the golden mean in both physical and intellectual life. That's another point our Greek colleague stressed. Always weigh up both sides of an issue. Even if you tend towards one side, keep the possibility open that the other side could be right, or right as well.

Listen to me, boy. I'm not telling you to sit on the fence; I'm just saying consider both arguments equally. I'll have to ask you leave now, though. I've got to go away for a few days, unexpectedly. I'll see you when I get back. Good night."

Exhausted, I walked back to Levi's house. Doubt is what characterizes the thinking man. That's one lesson Philo had drummed into me. Experience had taught me a second lesson, too. Thinking is exhausting; thinking things through is even more tiring. That must be the reason I'm so worn out.

M. EXPLANATION OR SUPPLEMENTATION?

I. Transforming

1. *Abraham's ordeal*

Philo hadn't given me a date. A few days later, I went back to
his house on the off-chance. I was shown in. Philo greeted me
heartily. "Delighted to see you again, Amos. You've become almost one of the family. I've missed you. So, go ahead."

"I'd like to come back to the point you touched on during
our previous conversation. The way you read the Bible; the allegorical interpretation of the texts. Levi gave me a couple of
pieces you wrote, one about Abraham and one about Moses. I
read them with admiration and amazement. Admiration because
I find your analyses so clever, and amazement because you read
the texts in such a different way from what's written."

"That's the key to allegorical interpretation, Amos. What the
text means is something quite different from what it says. It's all
about metaphors and I try to decipher them."

"I understand that, but when I was going through your work
on Abraham, which I read first, I was wondering what was interpretation and what was speculation."

"What do you mean?"

"Well, you admire the man, venerate him, that's clear. He was
chosen long before his birth to become an excellent man and rise
to great spiritual heights.[390] I was astonished when I read that.
Surely you don't believe in predestination?"

"No, I don't. A man builds his own life and is personally responsible for the result.[391] It's no accident that we're blessed with
reason. In some cases, though, the Lord gives us a little push.
That's how it was with Abraham; after all, the Lord had great
plans for the man."[392]

"Is that what you read in the text in Genesis? It doesn't say much
more than that Abraham left Ur, the city of the Chaldeans,[393] to

travel to Harran[394] with his father and immediate family and was then called by the Lord to go on without his family to 'a land to which I will guide you.'"[395]

"That's what it says, Amos, but what does it mean? It can't possibly just be talking about a random man travelling to another city without any particular reason. That really would be banal, unworthy of the Lord. No, what I actually suppose, I assume, is that this is about a spiritual migration. Abram, as he was then still known, felt called or was called to leave the material aspects of his existence behind, distance himself from the body, that 'base and polluted prison house' of the soul. In the world in which he had lived, he was engaged in astronomy. He believed you could deduce what would happen to us on Earth from the course of the stars.[396] The Creator didn't cross his mind.[397]

It was that world that Abraham left behind and it was only then that 'the Lord appeared to him.'[398] He hadn't previously been visible to him, attached as he was to the material world. Take note, Amos, what's written is that the Lord appeared to Abraham, not that Abraham saw the Lord.[399] It was only then that He changed his name from Abram to Abraham[400] and the Lord concluded a covenant with him.[401] That name change is highly significant."

"What do you mean, Philo?"

"Well, Abram means 'exalted father.' It's a contraction of the Hebrew word *Av* – father – and *ram*, the Arabic word for exalted. Now Abraham means something quite different, namely 'chosen father of the sound.' Sound refers to speech and speech to spirit.[402] The Lord saw in Abraham a wise and wonderful person; more a friend than a person."[403]

"A real eulogy, Philo. Up to a certain point, I agree with you. Abraham was a great and courageous man, prepared to give his all for a future as bright as it seemed unlikely: that he, an old, childless man would be at the root of many nations.[404] But you're putting him on a pedestal that reaches almost to heaven. You're turning him into an unworldly, spiritualized being. Such a figure could hardly have been the founding father of a people, of our people. That demands a doer, not a dreamer.

What's more, you're idolizing the man. You don't want to see his weaknesses."

"What do you mean, Amos?"

"I'm thinking about his behavior towards his concubine Hagar and their son Ismael. He sent them into the desert without much ado, probably to their deaths. At the insistence of his wife Sarah, admittedly, but he didn't put up much resistance."[405]

"The literal text doesn't bear witness to a high standard of morals and must, therefore, have another meaning. I read the text like this. Hagar is a symbol of what the Greeks refer to as 'preliminary studies:' worldly subjects, including maths, rhetoric, art and music. Only once these have been mastered can the way be paved for the study of philosophy and can one aspire to pure wisdom, which the Greeks call *Sophia* and I equate with the Lord. This is what Sarah symbolizes. Abraham had to rid himself of Hagar to reach spiritual maturity."[406]

"That's a rather complicated explanation; more of an apology for Abraham's behavior if you ask me. I get the impression that you're determined to find confirmation of your preconceived convictions in the text. You believe the mind strives to ascend, to gain knowledge of the divine world, which you call the 'real' world. Using intellect as its tool. Everything that reveals itself to the senses is an obstruction to attaining that goal.[407] In the same spirit, you grade knowledge: the worldly realms and, far above them, philosophy."

"Exactly. That's a good summary."

"That's not explanation, that's supplementation. You're adding to the text. I can't see it any other way, Philo."

"What I'm adding is what I feel Moses meant. That's explanation."

"Okay then, explanation, but it's still your explanation. Are you sure you've reached God's deeper grounds? I could easily provide a different explanation."

"Amos, the exegete! Go on, then."

I ignored his sarcasm. "Sarah hadn't had any children. At that time, that was a scandal in our society. A woman was looked down on for it. Evidently, the Lord didn't look kindly on her. Abraham slept with Hagar, Sarah's slave. Sarah had even suggested he should. Once Hagar was pregnant, her mistress 'was despised in her sight.' Hagar mocked Sarah.[408] So she had every reason to send her away. Abraham chose his wife of many years and abandoned his concubine. Understandable, although certainly no example of moral courage. A worldly explanation that fits better into our culture, don't you think?"

"No I don't. A vulgar explanation, without any depth, which adds nothing to our culture. It certainly doesn't bear a divine signature."

"Maybe, but which of the two is the right one?"

"The one that enriches our way of thinking."

"Reality is often vulgar. Reality shouldn't be embellished. In any case, I'm provoking you again, Philo. Your explanation of Abraham's name change seems contrived to me. I learned it a different way. In Babylon, Abram was the general name for a witness to an act of transfer. Abraham is, as I've said, a contraction of *Av* (Hebrew) – Father – and the Arabic *raham*, which means multitude. Ergo, Abram was called to bring many nations under God's wings."[409]

"Your teacher missed the point, young man, but enough of this." It sounded like an order. "Like you, boy, I don't give up. Your stubbornness is infectious. The theorem we are debating – the superiority of mind over matter – is confirmed in several biblical stories. Take the conflict between Cain and Abel and the story of the creation, for instance."

"Tell me, Philo, I'll be interested to hear."

2. *Fratricide*

"Abel, the younger of the two brothers, was a herdsman. I call

251

that a 'princely office.'[410] It encourages contemplation. You can see it as a general rehearsal for royal power. Wasn't David a shepherd boy? Cain, on the other hand, worked the soil, he was focused on matter, on inanimate material. The spiritualist as opposed to the materialist. Abel immediately offered the firstborn lambs to the Lord. Cain showed a flagrant lack of reverence. He ate the first fruits of the field himself and, a couple of days later, offered the inferior produce to the Lord. The Lord judges not the offering but the offeror. He saw a man looking upwards, who favored good, and a worldly figure who didn't shy away from wickedness. The first man's offering was accepted, but the second man's was rejected. This dichotomy was to pass from generation to generation."[411]

"So, in that story, why is Cain always named first, Philo?"

"Because the good are simply not noticed first. As I already said, what our senses show us is deceptive.[412] Here is the recurring message: follow the way of the spirit and avoid all that obstructs that way."

"A fine statement, Philo, but let's keep to the story. Why does the wicked one live and the good one die?"

"Haven't you understood yet, son? Because death isn't a punishment. On the contrary. 'Life which is in the flesh is not life.'[413] That only awaits our soul after death."

"But why is Cain – the personification of wickedness in your eyes – let off so lightly? Wouldn't corporal punishment be more fitting for his serious crime of fratricide?"

"Cain's punishment is worse. He was expelled by his family, secluded by all 'rational animals.'[414] A sign was put on him 'that no one should kill him who found him.'[415] And so the scourge continues."

"Cain was, nonetheless, blessed with rich progeny.[416] Surely, that must include a lot of bad characters. Shouldn't the Lord have spared the world that?"

"You're not making fun of me, are you, boy? No, wickedness in the ancestry doesn't guarantee wickedness in the progeny."

"I admire your ingenious analyses but, again, why should the Lord have presented the messages you read in the Holy Scriptures in such a complicated way? Why not just call a spade a spade?"

"Because symbolism encourages reflection, so it has far more impact than the literal text."

"That may be so, but I'd still prefer to read the text literally. It's already significant enough in my view. The Lord accepted Abel's offering and not Cain's, without giving any reason. That made Cain jealous. Evidently, the Lord underestimated the explosive force of the passion of jealousy. A miscalculation. Because the Lord realized he hadn't taken the right action, he let Cain live. He is a fair Being. What do you think of this rather 'worldly' interpretation?"

"Again, it's too base and, as far as the last point is concerned, it's inappropriate. You're judging God's decisions again. Who do you think you are?"

"Simply Amos, son of Mordechai. Believe me, Philo. What really concerns me is which of the many possible interpretations is decisive."

"I'll say it one more time: the explanation of someone who is philosophically learned, who has some knowledge of the Ideas world, who knows how to fathom the divine Logos. You're not in that category, Amos. Not yet, in any event."

"I'm too self-assured, Philo, I know."

"I'd like to leave the discussion there for this evening. I'll see you again tomorrow evening. Then I'll attempt to convince you that the Bible already refers to the polar relationship between body and spirit. Not openly, but allegorically. Until then."

3. *Sweet or bitter fruits?*

"Welcome, Amos: *shema* (Hebrew), listen.[417] Again, you'll hear a number of things that will sound odd but listen, hear them, absorb them and try to understand them." This is how Philo received me the following evening.

"I'm open to what you have to say, Philo, and I will respond."

"I've understood that; passivity is not your hallmark. And now, the story of the creation. The first man was initially just Idea, a minuscule element of God's unlimited Logos and, in that sense, a reflection of His spirit.[418] Thereafter, the Lord formed a material man, literally 'from the dust of the ground' and breathed 'the breath of life,' the soul, into him.[419] In the first man, body and soul achieved virtually perfect harmony."[420]

"May I interrupt you for a moment, Philo? Sometimes you talk about the spirit, sometimes the soul. Do you see them as synonymous?"

"No, Amos, even though the concepts are closely related. Spirit is everything immaterial in human existence. The soul is the diamond within the spirit, a true gift of God that encourages man to seek contact with the Giver. Let me just finish.

The body should have remained a sacred temple for the soul. It did so as long as the first man was still alone. Then woman was created. She was spoken to by the serpent, the symbol of pleasure. The serpent tempted her to eat a delicious-looking fruit, despite the Lord having forbidden it. From that fruit she gained 'wisdom,' worldly wisdom. [421] She also got her husband to eat some. And so they came together for the first time and learned about worldly pleasures. Since then, the soul has been beset with hedonism, the eternal lost from sight all too often in favour of the worldly, the fleeting.[422] Later generations have never achieved the perfection of the first man. Again, flesh versus spirit, a battle that will never end."

"You don't attribute a very honorable role to women, Philo."

"That's just the way things happened. It was, indeed, she who caused the first man to experience pleasure, so alien to the pure intellect,[423] but both are responsible. The Lord hadn't wanted it to be that way. He believed people would tend towards 'holiness and piety.'"[424]

"Another miscalculation, Philo?"

Philo shook his head and replied, grumpily, "I already said several times that I view the Lord as pure reason, pure wisdom. He doesn't make mistakes. Man mistook His intentions, picked the fruits expecting them to be sweet, but they proved bitter." He paused for a moment. "You don't look very convinced."

"Your exegetic capacity is impressive, virtually boundless, I'll say it again, but I have my doubts. You seem to live not only in what you call the 'real world' but also in what I've termed as the 'third world,' the world of the imagination.[425] Sometimes it's as if your imagination runs away with you."

"That may be so, but in the right direction, I feel."

"That's exactly what I'm not sure of, Philo. I'll give you another alternative interpretation, off the top of my head. The Lord was putting the first people to the test. Did he create idiots, or beings with an insatiable hunger for knowledge and wisdom? They passed that test. Their so-called sin would prove a blessing in disguise."[426]

Philo remained calm, smiled and laid a hand on my shoulder. "You're evidently aware that 'God's word is no longer in heaven.'[427] We do the Lord an injustice if we don't attempt to fathom the depths of His wisdom. That's what I try to do, but I don't claim to have the last word. You're evidently on the right path. I'd like to drop this topic now. There's no point in going round in circles.

"Just one more thing, if you'll allow me."

Philo didn't react, so I continued, "You read our scriptures allegorically, rather than literally. Aren't you afraid your readers will conclude that God's rules no longer need to be followed literally, either?"

"There is that risk, but I've expressly warned about that.[428] Following the Law and understanding the Law are two different things."

There was a knock at the door. A servant came in. "The

president of your synagogue is at the door. He needs to speak to you urgently."

"Let him in, Samuel" he replied and then turned to me, saying, "I'll have to leave it there for this evening. I'm sure you understand. Come back at the same time tomorrow evening."

II. Fantasizing

I was half an hour early, which surprised Philo. "This is a first, Amos. Is there something wrong?"

"Well yes, Philo, I was feeling restless, sad."

"What's happened, my boy?"

"This is my last visit. This morning I got a message that my ship will be sailing to Jaffa early tomorrow morning. I have to take it."

There was a long silence. It was Philo who broke it. "I'm sad about that, too. I'll miss you. I've never met a young person like you in Alexandria. For the people here, I'm the prototypical philosopher and you think twice before contradicting such a man. You're headstrong, but I've liked that."

"I've found you an extraordinarily fascinating and wise man, even though I've often disagreed with you."

Philo continued abruptly. "Right, then, what's your next and last point?"

"I told you that I've read your treatise on Moses, too. I've got such a different picture of the man from the one you paint."

"So, what's your picture like?"

"Like Abraham, I see a man before me, a man with his strong and his weak points. Not, as you said, someone who was 'the greatest and most perfect man that ever lived.'"[429] A humble[430] and courageous man, willing to assume the task of bringing 'the Israelites out of Egypt,' even if he did need quite some persuading.[431]"

"He had his weak points, too, you say. So what are they?"

"I think that's pretty obvious from the text. He never really succeeded in reining in our recalcitrant, oppositional people.[432] He was continually discouraged, wanted to give up, once even asked the Lord to end his life.[433] You praise him for his self-control, but he actually had quite some difficulty keeping his temper.[434] You're full of praise for his moral qualities,[435] but his copybook doesn't seem to be entirely un-blotted in this respect. The people started suspecting nepotism and not entirely without foundation. It would have to be his own brother, Aaron, who was appointed by the Lord as the first High Priest. Might Moses have put in a good word for him? Korach wasn't entirely unjustified in speaking to Moses about it.[436] The Lord punished him unmercifully for that.

Even his brother Aaron remarked on Moses' monopolising attitude. 'Has the Lord indeed spoken only through Moses?' he asked, 'Has He not spoken through us as well?' Moses didn't answer. He left that up to the Lord, who expressed his fury in no uncertain terms.[437] And don't you think, too, Philo, that Moses dismisses Aaron's bad behavior with unusual, if not incomprehensible, mildness. It's on Aaron's advice that the people make an image during Moses' absence: the golden calf. Aaron blames the people and gets away with it.[438] The people are heavily punished. Isn't that brotherly protectionism? You wonder 'whether it was a human mind or a divine intellect, or something combined of the two that had its abode in his body.'[439] I reply without hesitation that it was purely human. That doesn't detract from him in any way, in my eyes. There are no faultless people. That applies to great minds, too."

"Enough, Amos, your judgement of Moses is way off."

"But I'm quoting verbatim from your own works."

"Now that's the stumbling block. I've repeatedly tried to get that into your head. He disguises himself, presents himself as an average person in order to be recognizable to ordinary people. But he wasn't ordinary; he was extraordinary."

"There you go again, putting him on some kind of throne, Philo, like you did with Abraham."

"Absolutely. In his *Politeia*, Plato describes the ideal leader of a state, namely a king who is also a philosopher. Moses was such a man.[440] He'd freed himself from the shackles of worldly needs and passions, risen above the sensorial world and been granted access to the world of true knowledge.[441] He was able, like no other, to distinguish subjective opinions from objective knowledge. That also made him an excellent, unequalled lawgiver. The king became, as it were, 'at once a living law and the law a just king.'[442]

"I don't quite understand, Philo. Moses wasn't a king. He wasn't anointed. He didn't have much power at all, let alone absolute power. It was the Lord who led us through the desert and kept us alive.[443] The Lord was our king and Moses His executor, His delegate.

Was Moses wise? Yes, of course, but he wasn't omniscient. He became overworked and was convinced by his father-in-law, Jethro, to delegate his work to a number of 'capable men . . . men who fear God.'[444] Was he our lawgiver? You can't prove that, Philo."

I was shocked to hear myself. Behave yourself, I thought. This is our last discussion.

"The Lord is our lawgiver, isn't he, Philo? Not Moses. And that's what's so special. Amongst our neighbors, that was a royal prerogative. Our laws are binding and unchanging specifically because they have divine origins. They omit 'no one particular which they ought to comprehend.'[445] The Lord is our lawgiver and Moses his secretary."

Philo shifted into a more comfortable position. "Such passion, young man. Be careful, but go on."

"You describe an ideal: a brilliant king, also an unequalled legal scholar, who combines wisdom with justice and keeps that up all his life. The world has never yet produced such a figure."

"Oh yes it has, Amos. Moses embodied that ideal. There was a good reason for choosing him as our leader. And a second one will probably never be born. You're right about that." Philo's tone became fatherly and comprehending.

"The Lord led us, that's true, son, but not from on high. Being pure spirit, He doesn't possess the tools for actively putting his leadership into practice. That task was given to Moses."

"So you see Moses as a kind of incarnate Logos?"

"That's close to the way I see it. And yes, I do see Moses as our lawgiver. The Lord manifests Himself not in words, in spoken language, but in other signs. He enabled Moses to receive, record, decode and write down those divine signals. He made God's ideas accessible to us. Don't forget that not only the Jews but also almost all other nations respectfully adopt and honor these laws, particularly those nations that make the greatest account of virtue."[446]

"But, Philo, I don't know of a single nation that has adopted our laws."

"Not yet, son, but that will certainly come."

"Maybe so, but aside from that, your praise goes on. You classify Moses as an ideal king and lawgiver, even promoting him to the role of the first High Priest. He must fulfil that function, you write, because a king and lawgiver should devote attention to not only human, but also divine affairs. Why? Because 'the affairs of neither kings nor subjects go on well except by the intervention of divine providence.'[447] My problem, Philo, is that it didn't happen like that. The Lord expressly placed spiritual responsibilities in Aaron's hands.[448] He wanted a separation of worldly and spiritual authorities. The spiritual leader ensures that his worldly counterpart doesn't water down or exceed moral boundaries by too much."

"You're still at a superficial level, Amos, you're not thinking this through. Aaron was a good man, but not a strong character. You've said so yourself. Of course the Lord knew that Aaron was High Priest in name, ceremonial High Priest if you like; Moses was the actual High Priest."

"That's not written anywhere, Philo." The man is fantasizing,

I thought to myself. He's painting the picture of almost a demi-god. A non-existent figure. I said nothing for the time being. Philo didn't respond.

"You attribute one more function to Moses, that of a prophet. I fully agree with you there. He's the only one who has communicated directly with the Lord,[449] but you give this such a remarkable twist. You say he has to fulfil this function so 'he might through the providence of God learn all those things which he was unable to comprehend by his own reason.' And you continue, that 'what the mind is unable to attain to, that prophecy masters.'[450] Surely that's not the function of a prophet, Philo. A prophet is, above all, God's spokesman, conveying what He expects of us and how He judges our current actions."

"You're an enthusiastic critic, Amos. My answer is: yes, but I stressed another aspect of the prophet that was fundamental to Moses' function as a lawgiver."

"You're an invincible opponent, Philo. Allow me one more question, if you will. In view of the time, it will be the last."

"Don't be shy, boy. Make sure it's a real spiritual corker," he laughed.

"Well, the way you describe the figure of Moses, it seems as if you had sources other than Moses' own Scriptures alone."

"What makes you say that?"

"You write, for example, that the young Moses was 'a fine and noble child to look upon . . . more perfect than could have been expected at his age,' 'attending diligently to every lesson of every kind which could tend to the improvement of his mind,' that 'in a short time he surpassed all their knowledge, . . . so that everything in his case appeared to be a recollecting rather than a learning.' You call Moses an ascetic, who shunned luxurious life and 'never provided his stomach with any luxuries beyond those necessary tributes which nature has appointed to be paid to it, and as to the pleasures of the organs below the stomach he paid no attention to them at all, except as far as the object of having legitimate children was concerned.' 'He desired to live for his soul alone, and not for his body,' you say. What's more, 'he . . . brought under due command every one of the other passions' and 'administered severe punishment' to them.[451] Should I take all that as allegorical interpretation?"

"No, son. I mean that literally."

"Are you not then adding all kinds of ideas of your own to Moses' texts off your own bat, or are you fantasizing? Fascinating fantasies, but your fantasies, nonetheless."

"Well, Amos, it's always been my habit to combine what I've been told with what I've read. So I feel I know Moses' life better than most other people."[452]

"Told by whom?"

"By 'the elders of my nation.'"[453]

"Not the elders from our people, but Greek elders, I assume. Your additions often seem to fit perfectly with Greek ideals."

"I don't deny it, Amos. What I do deny, though, is fantasizing. It's not the right term. What it is, is imagining, forming images of things that are not there in the perceivable, measurable world – but could be.[454]

Fantasizing is something quite different. That's making things up. People use fantasy to convince themselves that a longing that remains unfulfilled has come true. Such fantasies are generally fleeting, coming and going without leaving a trace or, at most, leaving a feeling of disappointment. Fantasy satisfies certain needs or desires, temporarily, but doesn't generate any new points of view. Imagining is a creative process. It advances an individual and, in the best cases, societies as a whole, as well. Thanks to the power of imagination, Moses and his works have come to life for me. He's no longer a historical figure; he's become a living reality."

"So you've granted yourself access to what, a few days ago, I termed the third world, the world of imagination.[455] A world in which I, too, like to move."

I was quiet for a moment and so was Philo. "So, finally, we

converge, Philo. On this point, at least. You're more of a relativist than I'd been able to deduce from your writings."

Philo sighed deeply. "We have to say goodbye soon, Amos. Unfortunately, as far as I'm concerned. Let's not make it theatrical."

I understood he was letting me go first. "I've never met anyone I disagreed with so much but from whom I've nevertheless learned so much."

"Amos, I have never met anyone who spoke to me with such bravura but with whom I was unable to really get angry. I've come to see you almost as a rebellious son."

"That makes me proud, Philo. I've gained a great deal of respect for you. You speak with so much authority and dare to introduce ideas that clash with the established order. That takes intellectual courage, the ability to remain unbowed even when you take a furious beating."

"I appreciate your praise, my boy, and your criticism, too. I hope that, from your side, you'll reflect on the points of which you've been critical. I'll say it one more time. You don't have to embrace them to appreciate them for what, in my opinion, they are: levers to prevent spiritual ossification. Don't let any blind spots form in your vision."

"You've already convinced me of that, Philo. I'd like to add this to your words: you don't have to embrace notions to have great admiration for the one who generates them. You're an example to me. You'll never be far from my thoughts."

"Now then, that's enough son." He stood up. I followed. Philo threw his arm around my shoulders and, together, we walked to the front door.

"I'm sad to see you go, Amos. May your wisdom continue increasing and may contentment be your portion. *'Ken yehi ratzon* (Hebrew), let it be His will."

He waved me off. I could feel the tears running down my cheeks.

CHAPTER 9

_____

THE ANSWER: I AM BECOMING

*Keep doubting, son. Doubt prevents intellectual arrogance, stubborn-
ness and nit-picking.*

What man is he that can know the counsel of God? Or who can
think what the will of the Lord is? For the thoughts of mortal
men are miserable, and our devices are but uncertain.

The Wisdom of Solomon 9:13–14

A. LABYRINTH

A couple of weeks later I was back home.

"So, has your spiritual quest got you any further?" asked my
father.

"I've become wiser, Father, but no more certain."

"No more certain of what?"

"Of my identity, of who I am, who I want to become and who
I want to be, a Jew who honors his God and his people."

"Well, you're asking a lot, Amos, but tell me about your experiences."

"There are too many to mention, Father. I was inundated
with opinions and views. I felt as if I'd strayed into a labyrinth."

"Did you find a way out?"

"Not really, Father. No two people said the same thing. They
often contradicted one another."

"So, what did you discuss?"

263

Fig. 10 A portrayal of Abraham heeding the Lord's call and
travelling with his wife Sarah, his nephew Lot and his servants to
the land the Lord would show him (Gen 12:1).
Mosaic from Saint Mark's Basilica in Venice.
From: Guadalupi, G. (2011). *De Bijbel. Een vertaling in beelden.*
[The Bible, a translation in images]. Ten Have.

Abraham takes new paths without any notion of where they
will lead him. A creative spirit with courage; an example for the
thinking man.

"As I said, Father, many things: I can't give you more than a few examples. I'd thought there would be some agreement as to the image people have of the Lord. Nothing could be further from the truth! For one he was a completely transcendental greatness, not of this world and not in this world. Another painted an image that was quite recognizable for me, that of a kind of Super Moses, a human-like mentor carefully guiding humanity in its voyage through time. Yet another, it turned out, interpreted the Lord as an experience, as a mode of perception, as an inner state, and the question of how far that state is generated internally or by external influence was left ambiguous. I found this last vision rather appealing, Father. The Lord interpreted – perceived, actually – as a majestic and mysterious emotion."

"That's quite a minimalist image of God, son."

"I've had enough of it for the moment, Father, but let me finish.

The subject of immortality came up. Is death final and irrevocable? Yes, it is, I heard from some. Our end is an absolute end. Others believe that the soul survives, leaves the body and returns to its presumed birthplace: God's being. They see the soul as a quantity that can exist independently from the body. I find that idea odd, Father. After all, you can't separate the color of a flower from its bearer, can you? Some in that camp go even further, it seems. At some point, they believe, the body will be raised again and reunited with its soul. That, to me, is spiritual extremism. A dead body doesn't rise again; it rots away."

"Don't be so apodictic, Amos. The idea may stem from hope. The thought of death and dying frightens a lot of people."

"So do you have to kid yourself, Father?"

"Don't jump to conclusions, son. Not even you can look beyond the bounds of earthly life. But never mind, go on."

"The idea that the end time is near was brought up repeatedly. It turns out to be more widespread than I'd thought."

"That's probably down to all the suffering our people have gone through over the past few centuries and the difficult circumstances under which we live now. The idea is that the end of the tunnel is in sight and, there, hope dawns."

"For some, in the apocalyptics' view, Father, don't forget that. They believe we will all be judged for moral purity. If you're found lacking, then you can abandon all hope. Eternal suffering is the prospect you're faced with. Hope is only for those who have been found pure to the core. The 'final judgement' is supposed to be the sword of Damocles hanging above our heads. A source of hope and fear, in other words. Hope and fear, that's a mixture that can give you a good internal shake-up, in my eyes."

"Unless I'm very much mistaken, though, not everyone shares such apocalyptic ideas."

"Certainly not, Father; priests see them as pernicious fairy tales. I sympathize with them. For my part, I can't stand such extreme dualist thinking. It's either black or white. As if there were not a legion of shades of grey."

"We have no idea whether the Lord recognizes or acknowledges such nuances, son. Moses, for one, made a sharp distinction between blessing and cursing. 'A blessing, if ye obey the commandments of the Lord your God and a curse, if ye will not obey the commandments of the Lord your God.'"[456]

"I perceive the Lord as an extremely nuanced thinker, Father, but let me go on. I was introduced to a new concept: predestination. That was in Qumran. The idea is that the Lord has already globally established our destiny in advance, before we were born; some of us are destined for the right path; others a dead end. I find that idea strange, too, Father. The Lord created emancipated individuals, not puppets. He freed slaves; he didn't create them. He is curious as to how we will do in life on our own. I can't for the life of me imagine where such ideas come from. I only encountered them in the Qumran community, incidentally."

"Again, go easy, my boy. Man isn't made of iron. He is independent, yes, in principle responsible for his own actions, yes, but he's often afraid of accepting that. He's not so keen to be his own master, preferring to relinquish the responsibility, preferably to the Lord."

"That may be so, Father, but I don't think the Lord will accept such shirking."

"He is patient, son, that's how I see it, hoping for spiritual growth from His ultimate creation."

"A Lord who cherishes hope, just as we do, who doesn't control everything, that idea appeals to me, Father. I also spoke of hope myself, by the way, particularly about the figure of the Messiah, for me the personification of hope. Opinions are greatly divided on that topic, too. The whole idea is fiction, is what I heard. Man will have to extract himself from the mire on his own. Others are of the opinion that a Messiah will appear and found a kingdom of God, either on Earth or in heaven. I can't imagine the latter, Father."

"There's so much more that I can't imagine, son, and which I nonetheless assume exists."

I ignored his comment. "There are even those who believe the Messiah is in our midst."

"You mean the followers of Joshua, the carpenter's son from Nazareth."

"I do. I talked with the man a number of times, but with the Messiah? He turned out to be a complex, unfathomable, tragic figure. An odd combination of certainty and doubt, hope and despair, with an urge for self-destruction and self-glorification. Someone who ignored the line we Jews are supposed to draw between the sacred and the profane. A Jew who professed to be true to the Teachings but thoughtlessly trampled them underfoot. A passionate visionary, but with a vision that, in my view, led him to a dead end. I've already discussed this with you. He often claimed to be God's emissary on Earth. He came close to blasphemy. That's the way our authorities saw it, in any event. A man lost within himself. Nonetheless, he prompted reflection, self-examination. For me, at least. And that's no unnecessary luxury. He died too young."

"Have you got the gall to see yourself as some kind of religious authority superimposed on ours? Know your place! Did you have any more of these interesting encounters?"

"Yes, Father, I met a certain Yochanan, known as the Baptist. Like Joshua, a dyed-in-the-wool apocalyptic. The end time is coming, he roared at his followers. Repent, have yourself baptized and try to have your sins forgiven. For him, baptism turned out to mean immersion in the Jordan. Washing sins away. What an idea!

The practice wasn't new to me, incidentally. In Qumran moral purity was a real obsession. Being a 'child of the light' proved a vulnerable position. One false move and you lose it. So they bathed daily. They 'baptized' themselves every day, as it were."

"You speak so condescendingly of others, son. You have to take people as they come. Don't put yourself on a pedestal. It doesn't suit you and it could lead to a nasty fall."

"You're right, Father, but Yochanan irritated me. He spoke with such aplomb without saying who'd granted him that authority. He baptized 'as a sign of your new life.' It wasn't clear to me what he meant by that. I suspect he was referring to an eventual life in something like a divine paradise. That would be a flight from reality. You'll have to build a new life here, on Earth."

"A little bit of heaven grafted onto terrestrial ground, he may also have meant that by 'new life.'[457] Try to include metaphors in your thinking, Amos."

"Certainly they are important, Father, but they can also lead you too far from reality.

Talking about purity, I notice that purity has also started playing a really big role in our community. Ritual purity, I mean. Priests are demanding that we enter the Temple pure. I understand that, though. Such ritual is certainly nothing new to us. The legal scholars go much further, though, demanding that we rigorously observe the rules at home, too. That's not only a far-from-easy task; it also complicates contact with gentile compatriots. And that can only lead to further alienation. I don't like that. I want to attempt to be a conciliator. Like you, as I understand from our conversation."

"That does you credit, son."

"The encounter that had the biggest impression on me, though, Father, was with Philo. An intellectual heavyweight with a tremendous exegetic capacity and empathy for his fellow man. In my view, he crosses the line, too, though, like Joshua but in a completely different way. He turned out to rely very heavily on Greek philosophy. To put it irreverently, he saddles the Lord with a body he calls the Logos. He claims the Lord conceived the blueprints for the Creation, but was incapable of executing them Himself. The idea is that He has an executive arm: the Logos. I asked him what status that Logos has. Is it part of God's being, are you talking about a divine attribute or an entity with a considerable degree of autonomy? I didn't get a clear answer. He did say, though, that the Lord communicates with man through the Logos."

"Do you think he was talking about the divine presence on earth, its immanent form: what we call the *Shechina* (Hebrew)?"

"I don't think so. He sees the Logos more as a separate authority. I asked him, 'Is the Logos God's spokesman, as the prophet were, or does the Logos speak for itself?' Again, I got no clear answer. I was left with the question of whether that Logos eroded the tenet of the uniqueness and indivisibility of the Lord. 'Jerusalem' certainly wouldn't see that as an enhancement of the Teachings. And there's another point that has surprised me, Father, to put it mildly. You will think me self-important. A novice taking a renowned scholar to task, but my odyssey has made me audacious."

"Get to the point, boy!"

"Philo proved to be a dyed-in-the-wool exegete. He explains our Doctrine. Nothing special about that, in itself; many of our teachers do so. But he diverges rather far from the written text. He rewrites it, making it into his own stories. He wants to show that, essentially, Moses' scriptures differ little from those of the

Greeks, if you delve deep below the literal meaning. In fact, he believes the Greek sages have derived their ideas from those of Moses. He sees Moses as the greatest thinker of all time and the Greek sages as his successors. Highly unlikely, don't you think, Father? Moses' Scriptures weren't translated into Greek until hundreds of years after the death of Plato and his ilk. Let's face it, it's hard to believe these Greek scholars all had a mastery of Hebrew or Aramaic. Imagination can go a long way, Father, but how far should it go? These are dangerous assumptions, too, in my opinion. They pave the way far too well for a Hellenization of our people. Such human wisdom could detract from divine wisdom."

"You really are very skeptical, son, too negative. God's word may be explained. Personal, human interpretations inevitably slip into such paraphrases. Savour them for what they are: the fallible work of men. No one is forcing you to accept them."

"There were many of Philo's interpretations that I was unable to savor, Father. They're ingenious, but I don't like the way they taste.

I won't dwell on my visits to Philo, though; I'd like to talk about one more encounter, the one with your old friend David. I felt very little affinity with him. He did prove to still be a staunch, uncompromising nationalist. A pious man, true. Too pious, in my opinion. He doesn't want to live under the yoke of a heathen Emperor. The Lord is his sovereign. He and those of a like mind are inciting war against the Romans. A disastrous idea! They believe the Lord is with them. Nonsense. The Lord doesn't support desperate daredevilry."

"I quite agree with you, son, but I don't like your tone. It's too apodictic, too aggressive. Ask questions. Don't come up with answers in advance."

"These extremists, Father; they're jeopardizing the very existence of our country. It's as if an evil spirit has entered them."

"An evil spirit infiltrating from outside?"

"I'm not expressing myself well, Father. The evil doesn't come from outside; it doesn't come from the Lord, or from Satan, his adversary, of whom I've heard talk. It comes from within. You can't externalize evil. Man himself can grow into a Satan. That theme also came up, Father."

"Let's leave it there for today, son. You look tired. Go and get some sleep. We'll continue this tomorrow. Good night."

B. DIALECTICS VERSUS DOGMA

"You've given me a good impression of your odyssey, son," began my father the following morning. "You're becoming critical, putting things into perspective. That's what I'd hoped would happen, but don't get above yourself.

Now you've seen for yourself how our people has become embroiled in undue debate, in what I call hyper-dialectics, in a clash about directions and even in the service of vulgar power politics. Consequently, our teachings have become considerably less cohesive. The Torah is no longer in heaven, the Lord himself said so.[458] Endeavour to understand it, is what He meant. So you can't expect any unanimity of opinion. You spoke of a labyrinth. A marketplace is a better metaphor.

Many things are for sale at that 'idea market.' Much is of excellent quality, but you can't buy everything. You don't need everything, not everything is to your taste and you can't afford everything. You have to make choices, but your choice need not be definitive. You can always buy more or exchange what you've already bought. The market is open at all times. So doubt will accompany you throughout your life. Is the choice you made back then still the right one? Many people are uncomfortable with that; they seek certainty, making choices for life; after all, doubt is inextricably bound up with uncertainty. Doubt doesn't mean you are unable to choose, though. You certainly can choose, but you retain the option to decide this was not the right or the final choice. Keep doubting, son. Doubt saves us from intellectual arrogance, smugness and pedantry, which ultimately lead to intolerance and the inability to listen to others.

In time, you'll notice you become more critical, more of a spiritual epicure, as what you refer to as your inner self takes on an increasingly personal and pregnant allure.

You may wonder whether our world view is becoming something of a hotchpotch. No: it qualifies as a strongly differentiated, but nevertheless cohesive system. Taking the image of an ordinary market once again, there are two constants: the place where the market is held and the stalls where the wares are laid out.

Our 'idea market' also has two constants. Firstly, the belief in one unique, indivisible God. Secondly, the unconditional acceptance of the code of conduct and morals set down by Moses in his scriptures. The schemes[459] our sages have woven from these may be divinely inspired, but they're manmade. They should be studied diligently, but they're not binding.

The two constants I mentioned are what bind us together. Our people remains one big family, despite profound differences of opinion.

You must make your choice from all those 'weavings,' Amos. Not lightly or non-committally, but after careful internal consideration. Which of them hold significance for me and which can enrich and enhance my life? Slavishly following rules that fail to fulfil those criteria is hypocritical, in my view."

"Highly apt imagery, Father. That's indeed how my future will be, I realize that now. Physically, I'll probably be bound to one place. But mentally I won't. I'll regularly stroll through that 'idea market.' Tasting, testing, with my head and with my heart. Seeking my own way, a way that may well deviate considerably from the path many see as normative.

Who am I and who do I want to be? How should my 'inner self' look? That was the issue that launched me on my quest, on your advice. Now, I see the way – the way out – before me. There's no ready-made package awaiting me. I, myself, will have to forge a path through a forest of possibilities, a path marked with permanent discussion. A path with no clearly-defined destination.

In other words: I'll never get there. I am becoming, and that genesis is without end. I'll always be on my way. Spiritually, I'll be a wandering Jew. The destination will forever evade me, like the horizon when you endeavour to approach it."

"An exhilarating prospect, my son! The Lord bless you and keep you while on that path.[460]

Come on, though, let's get back to work."

ABBREVIATIONS OF TITLES OF PHILO'S WORKS CITED IN ENDNOTES

Abr.	De Abrahamo	On Abraham
Aet.	De Aeternitate Mundi	On the Eternity of the World
Agr.	De Agricultura	On Husbandry
Conf.	De Confusione Linguarum	On the Confusion of Tongues
Congr.	De Congressu Eridutiones gratia	On Mating with the Preliminary Studies
Decal.	De Decalogo	The Decalogue
Flacc.	In Flaccum	Against Flaccus
Hyp.	Hypothetica/Apologia pro Iudaeis	Hypothetica: Apology for the Jews
Leg. All.	Legum Allegoriarum	Allegorical Interpretation
Mig.	De Migratione Abrahami	On the Migration of Abraham
Mos.	De Vita Mosis	On the Life of Moses
Mut.	De Mutatione Nominum	On the Change of Names
Opif.	De Opificio Mundi	On the Creation
Plant.	De Plantatione	Concerning Noah's Work as a Planter
Post.	De Posteritate Caini	On the Posterity of Cain and his Exile

Praem.	De Praemiis et Poenis	On Rewards and Punishments
Prov.	De Providentia	On Providence
Quaest. In Gn.	Questiones et Solutiones in Genesim	Questions and Answers on Genesis
Quaest. In Ex.	Questiones et Solutiones in Exodum	Questions and answers on Exodus
Quod Omn. Prob.	Quod omnis Probus Liber sit	Every Good Man Is Free
Sac.	De Sacrificiis Abelis et Caini	On the Birth of Abel and the Sacrifices Offered by Him and by Cain
Som.	De Somniis	On Dreams, That They are God-Sent
Spec. Leg.	De Specialibus Legibus	The Special Laws
Virt.	De virtutibus	On the Virtues
Vit. Cont.	De Vita Contemplativa	On the Contemplative Life or Suppliants

OTHER ABBREVIATIONS

O.G.J.   Flavius Josephus. (1996) *De oude geschiedenis van de Joden* [The Antiquities of the Jews] Translated into Dutch by Meijer and W.A. Wis. F.J.A.M. Amsterdam: Ambo.

J.W.   Flavius Josephus. (1982) *The Jewish War*, Cornfeld, G. (Ed) Grand Rapids: Zondervan Publishing House.

ENDNOTES

1. This Biblical wisdom literature provides practical life lessons and reflections on such profound issues as the point of our existence the essence of the Creator. The individual is the central focus rather than the community as in other books of the Hebrew Bible. There is little or no mention of themes such as the Temple service, Exodus and the Covenant. The wisdom of the writer is a God-given gift.

2. Ecclesiastes 8:16–17

3. Ecclesiastes 1:2–3

4. Ecclesiastes 1:3

5. Ecclesiastes 1:9

6. Ecclesiastes 1:8

7. Multatuli. The Prayer of the Ignorant. In: complete works I. Amsterdam: van Oorschot, 1862/1950

8. Ecclesiastes 7:27–29

9. Isaiah 53:2–12

10. He died in 4 BCE (see further in Foreword).

11. See: J. Sacks. We are what we remember. Covenant and Conversation, 21 September 2016.

12. Archelaus, one of Herod's sons, succeeded him in Judea. He was deposed by the Romans in the year 6 CE for maladministration (see further under Foreword).

13. Priestly and moneyed aristocrats were jointly referred to as Sadducees. The name is derived from the Hebrew word Zeduqi, descendants of Zadok, the first High Priest in the First Temple, built by King Solomon. Naturally, the term only applies to the priestly caste, but the Essenes also considered themselves to be Zeduqi (see chapter 5).

14. The highest law school in Judea, made up of Sadducees and Pharisees, under the presidency of the High Priest.

15. The words with which the Lord called Abraham to leave his old, familiar surroundings and journey to new, as yet unknown climes (Genesis 12:1).

16. The Lord tasked Moses with worldly affairs and his brother Aaron and

his descendants with priestly affairs. Pedigree was the primary criterion for the appointment of a High Priest (Exodus 28:1–2; Numbers 17:18–23).

17. Exodus 24:2–4
18. Numbers 12:7–8
19. Exodus 33:23
20. Leviticus 18:2–5
21. Leviticus 21:1, 11:2–3, 11:4–7 ; Deuteronomy 14 :6–8
22. Genesis 3:3
23. Ezekiel 18:2–3
24. Van Praag, H.M. (2008). *God en Psyche. De redelijkheid van het geloven. Visies van een Jood*. [God and Psyche. The reasonableness of believing. A Jew's views]. Amsterdam: Boom.
25. Ecclesiastes 8:16–17
26. The angel Lucifer tried to compete with the Lord. He became the leader of the fallen angels and was, finally, driven out of heaven, to continue as Satan, the devil.
27. Leviticus 15:2–3
28. Leviticus 19:19–20
29. Amos 5:4
30. Deuteronomy 30:19
31. Leviticus 17:11–12
32. Deuteronomy 30:19
33. Leviticus 21:1–4
34. Jeremiah 7:22
35. 1 Kings 6:13
36. Genesis 6:5–7, 11:4–9
37. Flavius Josephus. J.W. II, 166; Isaiah 58:6–7; Ezekiel 33:14–26; Amos 5:21–25
38. Deuteronomy 11:26–27
39. Exodus 28:1–2; 29:1
40. See the Foreword.
41. Flavius Josephus. J.W. II, 164
42. Deuteronomy 32 :4–5; Ezekiel 33:20
43. Dead Sea Scrolls 1Q, Community Rule, III, 24–26; XI 7–12, 17–18; 1QH, Thanksgiving Scroll, XII, 30–33, 38–40.
44. Deuteronomy 11:26–28
45. Dead Sea Scrolls 1Q, Community Rule, III, 18–21. Also see chapter 5
46. Deuteronomy 32:4
47. Genesis 6:5–6
48. 1 Samuel 15:3–23
49. Leviticus 19:18, 34
50. Deuteronomy 17:20–28
51. Numbers 12:2

52. Genesis 12:1
53. Genesis 12:2
54. Isaiah 43:12
55. Deuteronomy 30:19
56. Praag, H.M. van (2014). *Net voorbij de rede. Verkenningen op het grensvlak van vernuft en verbeelding.* [Just Beyond Reason. Explorations of the Border Region between Ingenuity and Imagination]. Amsterdam: Boom
57. Sacks, J. The Bessing of Love. Covenant and Conversation. 18 June 2016
58. Genesis 1:2
59. Flavius Josephus, J.W. II :163
60. Genesis 2:7
61. Leviticus 19:1
62. Exodus 34:6–7
63. Deuteronomy 30:12
64. Exodus 34:6
65. Deuteronomy 30:19
66. Leviticus 22:4
67. Isaiah 1:16–17
68. Isaiah 1:27
69. Flavius Josephus, O.G.J. XVIII:15
70. Flavius Josephus, J.W. II:165
71. Flavius Josephus, O.G.J. XVIII:18
72. Deuteronomy 30:15–20
73. Genesis 6:5–8
74. Flavius Josephus, J.W. II:162–163. Pirbei Avos (2009). *Spreuken der vaderen Joodse wijsheid uit de oudheid.* [Tales from the Fathers of Jewish Wisdom in Antiquity] Translation into Dutch: Rabbi R. Evers. Amsterdam: Stichting Salomon/Boom 20
75. Exodus 24:8
76. Leviticus 10:3
77. First due to the failed policies of the Hasmonean monarchs and then, roughly fifty years later, through the misconduct of the son of King Herod first, Achelaus, the Ethnarch of Judea. Also see the Foreword.
78. Leviticus 19:1, 34
79. See the Foreword.
80. Deuteronomy 4:25–28
81. Exodus 19:5
82. Flavius Josephus, J.W. II:66–75
83. Judges 7
84. 2 Maccabees 10:1–3
85. Zechariah 4:6
86. The underworld.
87. I Kings 11:1

88. Both kings from the Hasmonean house, John Hyrcanus from 134–104 BCE and Aristobulus I from 104–103 BCE.

89. I Kings 11:1

90. The Sanctification of God's name (*Kiddush Hashem*, Hebr.) is a central concept in Judaism. That Name is sanctified above all by following the path that He mapped out for man. In extreme cases, you are expected to give your life to prevent desecration of God's name. Martyrdom is neither sought nor glorified, though.

In the books of the Maccabees, there is one story that could lead you to think otherwise (2 Maccabees 7). Seven brothers and their mother were arrested and tortured to force them to eat pork. The brothers would rather "die than abandon the traditions of their forefathers" and, indeed, died a martyr's death. They were, however, convinced that "after our death, the King of this world will restore us to a new, eternal life because we have died for His scriptures." The mother "saw her seven sons die in a single day" but endured it with great courage.

The story has something or a heroic epic (2 Maccabees 7:3), a genre alien to Jewish philosophy. The books of the Maccabees were therefore not included in the Hebrew Bible.

91. Isaiah 2:4

92. Jewish house of religious learning

93. See the Foreword.

94. Leviticus 19:18

95. Dead Sea Scrolls Damascus Scripture 1 CD I:11–21

96. Nothing is known with certainty about the Teacher of Righteousness. He may have been a priest from the house of Zadok who was in conflict with his colleagues in Jerusalem and, in particular, with the first High Priest of the House of Hasmon: Jonathan (1 Maccabees 10:20). He supposedly "shed over Israel the waters of lies. He caused them to wander in a pathless wilderness." (Damascus Scroll I.14–15). The Teacher was probably tried and banished from Judea, along with his followers. The group later returned. How and when is unclear.

97. Genesis 1:2 English Standard Version

98. Genesis 1:2 Pentateuch and Haftara (1981) J.H. Hertz. (Ed.) London/ New York Soncino Press

99. Deuteronomy 18:10–13

100. Isaiah 55:8–9

101. Genesis 1:3–29

102. Genesis 1:27

103. Dead Sea Scrolls The Community Rule 1Q, III:12–25; Dead Sea Scrolls Hodayot 1QHa, XII:30–33; XII:38

104. See page 89, "What prompted it, Juda . . ."

105. Dead Sea Scrolls The Community Rule 1Q, III:12–25

106. Dead Sea Scrolls Damascus Scripture 1 CD, 1:11
107. Dead Sea Scrolls The Community Rule 1Q, V:2–3, 10–11
Zadok – the figure mentioned in this text – was the first High Priest of the first Temple, built during the reign of King Solomon. The Teacher of Righteousness was purported to be a descendant of Zadok. Members of the Qumran community call themselves Zadokites, sons of Zadok.
108. Dead Sea Scrolls The Rule of War 1Q, 1:11–14
109. Dead Sea Scrolls Habakkuk 1Q, VII:4–5
110. Exodus 19:20
111. Dead Sea Scrolls Habakkuk 1Q, XI:4, VIII:8–13; XII:1–12
112. Numbers 12:6–8
113. Dead Sea Scrolls The Rule of War 1QM, 1:10–15
114. Deuteronomy 30:12
115. Eruvin 13b
116. Dead Sea Scrolls The Community Rule 1Q III:12–25
117. Flavius Josephus, JW VIII:122
118. Genesis 1:28; Exodus 20:12; Deuteronomy 7:13–14, 26:11
119. Flavius Josephus, JW VIII:137–142
120. Flavius Josephus, JW VIII:143–144
121. Exodus 34:6
122. Leviticus 19:18
123. When Jacob was on his way to see Laban, the brother of his mother Rebecca – fleeing from his brother Esau – at the place where he spent the night he had a dream, in which "he saw a stairway resting on the earth, with its top reaching to heaven, and the angels of God were ascending and descending on it." He also saw the Lord, who promised to give the land on which he was lying to him and his descendants (Genesis 28:12–13). When Jacob awoke, he thought, "Surely the Lord is in this place (*hamakom*, Hebr), and I was not aware of it" (Genesis 28:16). In rabbinic literature, the place ha–Makom became a name for the Lord.
124. Dead Sea Scrolls New Jerusalem 2Q, 4Q, 5Q, 11Q, various fragments
125. Exodus 3:13–14
126. Flavius Josephus, JW, VIII:134
127. Dead Sea Scrolls The Community Rule 1Q, III:20–26
128. Flavius Josephus, JW, VIII:150
129. Flavius Josephus, JW, VIII:130–131, 123
130. Flavius Josephus, JW, VIII:131–133
131. Leviticus 19:2
132. A skin condition, the nature of which is unknown and that is deemed to make the sufferer unclean. The word is translated as leprosy, but the disease was still unknown in biblical times. *Tzaraäth* could affect not only the skin but also fabrics and walls (Leviticus 13:47; 14:34–35, 54–56). It may have been a fungal disease.

133. Proverbs 16:18
134. Hebr: He who repents, turns again to God. (See: Ezekiel 18:23, Ben Sira 21:6)
135. Isaiah 1:4
136. Jeremiah 11:11
137. Jeremiah 31:31–33
138. Ezekiel 37:1–2, 5–6
139. Dead Sea Scrolls Pseudo–Ezekiel, Fragment 2:1–9
140. Ezekiel 36:22–24
141. Ezekiel 18:25–26
142. Isaiah 40:3
143. Dead Sea Scrolls The Community Rule 1Q VIII:13–17
144. Habakkuk 1Q, VII:4–5
145. Ben Sira 28:4
146. Micah 6:8, Ben Sira 10:18
147. Deuteronomy 30:19
148. Luke 3:15
149. Luke 3:3
150. 2 Kings 1:8
151. Matthew 3:4
152. 2 Kings 2:1, 11
153. Malachi 3:23
154. Luke 3:3
155. Matthew 3:3; Mark 1:15
156. Luke 3:3
157. Matthew 3:3; Isaiah 40:3
158. See page 162, "I'm sure you know what the apocalypses are . . ."
159. See page 149, "The men in Qumran invoke the Teacher of Righteousness . . ."
160. Exodus 33:20–23
161. Genesis 2:7
162. Luke 1:15
163. Luke 3:10–14; Flavius Josephus, OGJ XVIII:117
164. Matthew 3:10
165. Matthew 3:7–9
166. Deuteronomy 1:26–28
167. Matthew 3:9
168. Matthew 3:11
169. Matthew 3:11
170. Flavius Josephus, OGJ XVIII:117
171. Luke 1:13–17, 76
172. Matthew 3:11
173. Mark 6:15

174. Luke 3:15
175. Matthew 3:14
176. Matthew 3:16–17
177. Luke 3:7
178. Luke 7:28
179. Luke 3:16
180. Matthew 3:14
181. Isaiah 2:12
182. Leviticus 19:2
183. On the Sabbath and on feast days, the congregation reads from the five books of Moses, the Sidra of the week and then passages from one or another of the books of the Bible, generally the Prophets. The content of the *Haftarah* is related to that of the Sidra. Each Sidra has its own specific *Haftarah*.
184. Luke 4:16–21
185. Isaiah 61:1–3
186. Luke 4:22
187. Capernaum, from *Kfar Nahum* (Hebr.), Nahum's village.
188. Luke 4:23
189. Luke 4:24
190. Luke 4:29
191. Mark 3:11–12; Matthew 26:63–64
192. See under Introduction.
193. Flavius Josephus. O.G.J. XX:97–98
194. See under Foreword.
195. John 4:2
196. Matthew 3:11
197. Luke 5:20–21, 24
198. Matthew 20:28
199. Luke 5:21
200. Kafarnaum, derived from Kfar Nahum (Hebr): the village of Nahum
201. Luke 4:33 – 35
202. Acts 19:13–16
203. Luke 4:34
204. Here, the speaker is referring to the numerous, often apocalyptic works written in the inter-testamentary period that are not included in the Canon. They recount revelations the writer has received from a heavenly figure, often the Lord, sometimes through the agency of angels. They are referred to as pseudepigrapha because many of them have been attributed to someone other than their real (unknown) author. These are often well-known biblical figures, such as Enoch, Solomon and Moses, possibly to lend the scripture more credence.
205. Enoch is mentioned in Genesis (5:18–25) as the seventh descendant of Adam, but plays no further role in the Bible. According to tradition, he was a

God-fearing man, who did not die but, like the prophet Elijah, is said to have been assumed directly into heaven.

There are two books bearing his name. In Enoch 1, the last part talks about the fall of the angels. Enoch 2 tells how Enoch was initiated into the secrets of the creation process.

The Book of Jubilees is a work in which the stories from Genesis and the first few chapters of Exodus are retold in the form of mysterious revelations that Moses is said to have received on Mount Sinai. The book is named Jubilees because it adheres to the biblical period as a time unit for describing history: a period of 49 (7 times 7) years, as mentioned in Leviticus 25:5.

This book, too, describes angels rebelling against the Lord, being banished from heaven and being held responsible for the evil in the world.

206. Psalms 82:1

207. Satan was the leader of the fallen angels and was seen as a personification of evil in the world. In the Hebrew Bible, he does not appear as such. In the book of Job, Satan does appear on the scene, but as the accuser in God's court, the man who informs Him of transgressions people have committed.

Satan (Hebr.) means opponent, also accuser. In the Septuagint, the Greek translation of the Hebrew Bible, the word is translated as diabolos (devil).

In the Hebrew Bible, man himself is held responsible for evil. The Lord may occasionally act violently, but it is always to punish sins committed by or against the Jewish people.

In the Christian Bible and early Christendom, Satan was given a main role as the primary opponent of the Lord.

208. Latin for light bringing. The name refers to the King of Babel who, in a mocking song, Isaiah compares with a morning star fallen from heaven.

209. Deuteronomy 18:11–13; Leviticus 20:6–7

210. Mark 3:22

211. Mark 3:21, 31–32

212. Matthew 12:34, 23:13–33

213. Jeremiah 7:11

214. Luke 11:20

215. Luke 11:24–26

216. Matthew 9:34

217. Matthew 9:23–26

218. Matthew 10:1, 8

219. Matthew 4:18

220. Mark 8:27; Luke 9:18

221. Elijah is a prophet who did not die, but was taken up to heaven and will return as a herald of the Messiah (Malachi 3:23).

222. Luke 9:18–21; Matthew 16:20

223. Luke 8:8; Mark 4:9

224. Matthew 16:22–23

225. Matthew 16:22–23
226. Dan 8:24
227. Matthew 25:31–46
228. Matthew 17:23
229. Matthew 20:28
230. Leviticus 16:10, 34
231. Luke 6:1–5
232. Luke 6:6–11
233. Luke 5:27–32
234. Matthew 23:13–39
235. Mark 7:19
236. Leviticus 11
237. Matthew 9:6
238. John 14:9; Luke 12:8
239. John 3:16, 10:30
240. Matthew 16:27, 25:30–31, 26:64
241. Ezekiel 2:1; Job 25:6
242. Matthew 24:15
243. Dan 8:24
244. Dan 7:13–15
245. Mark 10:47–48
246. John 4:25–26
247. Matthew 16:16
248. Matthew 16:19
249. Mark 9:23
250. Luke 12:8
251. Luke 9:26
252. Matthew 25:32
253. Matthew 13:55
254. Luke 2:21
255. Luke 2:42
256. School of Jewish learning
257. Matthew 1:21; 3:17
258. Luke 1:32–33
259. Genesis 12:1–2; Exodus 3:4, 1 Samuel 3; Isaiah 6:8
260. Matthew 3:17
261. Isaiah 53:10
262. Isaiah 1:16–7
263. Isaiah 61:1–3
264. Matthew 5:3–10
265. Matthew 5:16, 39–42
266. Matthew 10:1–4
267. Matthew 16:17

268. Matthew 8:2–3
269. Matthew 26:63–64
270. Matthew 26:63–64
271. Matthew 25:31–46; 26:64; 24:31
272. The highest administrative and legal body in Judea.
273. Matthew 23:33
274. Matthew 26:53
275. A far more personal form of address for the father figure than the Hebrew term "*Av*."
276. During Pesach, the Jewish Passover, Jews celebrate the Exodus from Egypt. It is one of the three pilgrims' feasts that Jews in Jerusalem were supposed to celebrate there (Ex 23:14). The other two are the Feast of Weeks (Shavuot), celebrating the giving of the Torah, and the Feast of Tabernacles (Sukkot), in remembrance of the journey through the desert to the Promised Land.
277. Matthew 21:1–5
278. Zachariah 9:9
279. Matthew 21:13; Jeremiah 7:11; Matthew 6:24
280. Matthew 21:9
281. Matthew 21:22
282. During the Seder, in the domestic sphere, the story of the Exodus from Egypt is told. A chair is kept free for Elijah, the prophet who will return one day and announce the coming of the Messiah (Malachi 3:23–24).
283. Luke 22:16
284. Matthew 25:45–46
285. Luke 22:19
286. Luke 22:20
287. John 11:50
288. Isaiah 53:1–12
289. Isaiah 49:3–7
290. Matthew 26:56
291. Mark 15:18; Luke 23:27
292. Matthew 27:25
293. Praag H.M. van (2014). *Net voorbij de rede. Verkenningen op het grensvlak van vernuft en verbeelding*. [Just Beyond Reason. Explorations of the Border Region Between Ingenuity and Imagination]. Amsterdam: Boom.
294. Psalms 22:2; Matthew 27:46
295. Mark 9:23
296. Matthew 24:2
297. Matthew 5:18
298. Mark 7:5,19; Matthew 12:1–14; Mark 2:16–17
299. Matthew 21:21–22
300. Matthew 16:25

301. Mark 12:35–36
302. Jewish Law, the legal parts of the Talmud.
303. Mark 14:62–64
304. Luke 22:70
305. Luke 24:21
306. Deuteronomy 30:11–14
307. Alexander the Great (356–323 BCE) propagated the Greek language and culture in territories he conquered. His successors continued that policy. Greek became the world language. Many hybrid forms emerged of the Greek and local cultures. Large areas were Hellenized in this way. Judea and, above all, the Jewish communities were also affected (also see Praag, H.M. van (2014), *Net voorbij de rede. Verkenningen op grensvlak van vernuft en verbeelding.* [Just Beyond Reason. Explorations of the Border Region Between Ingenuity and Imagination] Amsterdam: Boom).
308. This section was part of the article in *Israël en de Kerk* [Israel and the Church], March 2016.
309. Praag H.M. van (2014). *Net voorbij de rede. Verkenningen op het grensvlak van vernuft en verbeelding.* [Just Beyond Reason. Explorations of the Border Region Between Ingenuity and Imagination.] Amsterdam: Boom.
310. *Tzitzit* are tassels that are wound in a particular way, with a bluish-purple thread incorporated. These days, they are worn by (orthodox) men on the *arba kanfot* (Hebr.), a square band around the waist, beneath the outer garments.

Tzitzit are also attached to the prayer shawl men wrap around themselves during morning prayers and in the synagogue during services that include readings from the Torah. (In liberal Judaism also by women.)

The *tzitzit* are supposed to remind Jews to "recall all the commandments of the Lord and observe them." (Numbers 15:38).

311. Opif.:8:17–19
312. Som.:37
313. Opif.:170
314. Spec. Leg I:33–36
315. Isaiah 2:2–3
316. Spec. Leg I:52
317. Spec. Leg. I:32
318. Spec. Leg I:13
319. Opif.:9
320. Leg. All. I:51; Virt. 65
321. Decal.:41
322. Aet.:13
323. Isaiah 2:4
324. Praem:165–172; Deuteronomy 30:1–10
325. Praem:167

326. Elohiem is a plural form often used in the Bible to indicate excess power (Pentateuch and Haftarots, J.H. Hertz (Red.), London, Soncino Press, 1981)

327. The term *Hashem* (Hebr.), the Name, is also used for the "empathetic God"

328. 1 Samuel 15:2–3

329. Opif.:10, 172; Leg. All:I:51

330. The plural of *yeshiva*, a Jewish school.

331. The High Court in Jerusalem, under the presidency of the High Priest.

332. Sandmel, S. (1979). Philo of Alexandria. An introduction, New York, Oxford: Oxford University Press.

333. In 334 BCE

334. Flacc:43

335. T. d. G. II:3–7; 69

336. Flacc. 41

337. T. d. G. II:80

338. T. d. G. II:89

339. T. d. G. II:8

340. T. d. G. II:32

341. Flusser, D. (1980). Judaism and the Origins of Christianity. Jerusalem: The Magnus Press.

342. Numbers 23:9

343. Isaiah 2:3

344. Spec. Leg. I:44–48; Leg. All. I:36–38, 41

345. Opif. :23–25, 134

346. Opif:171

347. Agr.:51

348. Conf.:171–175

349. Conf.:175, 179

350. Genesis 1:2

351. Deuteronomy 6:4–9

352. Proverbs 8:22–23; 30

353. Mos. II:12

354. Page 305 ff

355. Niehoff, Y.A. and M. Philo Judaeus, Enceclopaedia Judaica, second Edition, Vol 16

356. Page 40 ff

357. Prob.:149–154

358. Leviticus 19:18–4

359. Spec. Leg. I:44–49; Spec. Leg. III:5

360. Mos. I:158–159

361. Exodus 33:2–4:20

362. Van Praag, H.M. (2014). *Net voorbij de rede. Verkenningen op het grensvlak*

van vernuft en verbeelding. [Just Beyond Reason. Explorations of the Border Region Between Ingenuity and Imagination.] Amsterdam: Boom

363. Post.:14
364. Spec. Leg. I:46, 49
365. Opif:170–172
366. Isaiah 57:15
367. Isaiah 56:1–7; 58:6–10; Amos 5:21–24; Michah 6:8
368. Spec. Leg. III:5; Migr.:9
369. Opif. :136–137
370. Opif. :138
371. Opif. :140
372. Opif. :152
373. Opif.:151–152
374. Genesis 17:10–6
375. Spec. Leg. I:9
376. Migr.:168–169
377. Migr.:17–18
378. Deuteronomy 30:19
379. Leg. All III:16–17
380. Mos. I:25–26, 158
381. Numbers 11:10
382. Spec. Leg. III:1–5
383. Vit. Cont.:21, 24–26
384. Vit. Cont.:90
385. Spec. Leg.:1–6
386. Migr. II:9 III:13
387. Prob.:75–79; Hyp.:11–18
388. Leg. All. I:45
389. Mos. II:12–18
390. Mos. I:12, 17, 19
391. Deuteronomy 11:26–32
392. Genesis 12:1–2
393. Inhabitants of Mesopotamia, who were later to become the ruling class of Babylon.
394. Genesis 11:31–6
395. Genesis 12:4–5#
396. Abr. :68–69
397. Migr.:9,13
398. Genesis 17:1; Abr.:77
399. Genesis 12:7; 15:1
400. Genesis 17:5
401. Genesis 15:18; 17:1–8
402. Mut:66, 69; Quaest. in Gn.:# 43

403. Abr.:273
404. Genesis 17:3–6
405. Genesis 21:10–14
406. Congr.:6–21
407. Plant:36–37
408. Genesis 16:5–6
409. Hertz, J.H. (Ed) (1981) Pentateuch and Haftorahs. Hebrew text, English translation and Commentary. London/New York, Socino Press.
410. Quaest. in Gn. I:59
411. Quaest. in Gn. I:60–61
412. Quaest. in Gn. I:61
413. Quaest. in Gn. I:76
414. Quaest. in Gn. I:76
415. Genesis 4:15
416. Genesis 4:17–23
417. Here, Philo is referring to Deuteronomy 6:4. *Shema Yisrael* (Hebr.). These are the first words of the central prayer in Jewish liturgy, which incorporates the core principles of Judaism.

The concept of *Shema* is multifaceted. It means: listen, take note, hear, take heed, internalize, respond, absorb what I say. The word appears 92 times in the book of Deuteronomy alone (J. Sacks. The Spirituality of Listening. Covenant and Conversation, August 24, 2016).

418. Opif.:134
419. Genesis 2:7
420. Opif.:136
421. Genesis 3:6
422. Opif.:151–157; Leg. All.:44–55
423. Quaest. in Gn. III:10
424. Opif.:155
425. See page 268, "You don't have to embrace them to appreciate them . . ."
426. Van Praag, H.M. (2006). God en Psyche. De redelijkheid van het geloven. Visies van een Jood. [God and Psyche. The reasonableness of believing. A Jew's views Amsterdam: Boom.
427. Deuteronomy 30:12
428. Spec. Leg. IV:143
429. Mos. I:1
430. Numbers 12:3
431. Exodus 3:11; 4:1; 4:13
432. Exodus 15:24; 16:2–3; 17:2; Numbers 11:1,10; 17:6; 25:3
433. Numbers 11:10
434. Numbers 11:11; 20:9–12; 16:15; Mos. I:25–26
435. Mos. I:148; II:8–11
436. Numbers 16:1–14

437. Numbers 12:1–9
438. Exodus 32:22–25
439. Mos. I:27
440. Mos. II:2
441. Mos. I:25–26
442. Mos. II:4
443. Exodus 16:10–4; Numbers 9:15; Exodus 16:35–17
444. Exodus 18:21
445. Mos. II:12
446. Mos. II:17
447. Mos. II:5
448. Exodus 28:1–3
449. Numbers 12:7–8
450. Mos. II:6
451. Mos. I:18–29
452. Mos. I:4
453. Mos. I:4
454. Van Praag, H.M. (2014). *Net voorbij de rede. Verkenningen op het grensvlak van vernuft en verbeelding.* [Just Beyond Reason. Explorations of the Border Region Between Ingenuity and Imagination.] Amsterdam: Boom.
455. Mos. 2:6
456. Deuteronomy 11:26–29
457. Matthew 3:11
458. Deut 30:11
459. Ecclesiastes 7:29
460. Here, the father quotes a line from the benediction prayer Moses used to bless the Jewish nation (Numbers 6:24–26).

SELECTED BIBLIOGRAPHY

Ben-Sasson, H.H. (Eds) (1976). A History of the Jewish People. Cambridge: Harvard University Press.

Berlin, A., Brettler, M.Z. (Eds) (2004) The Jewish Study Bible. Oxford: Oxford University Press.

Cohen, S.J.D. (2006). From the Maccabees to the Mishnah. Louisville/London: Westminster John Knox Press.

Flusser, D. (1984). *Tussen oorsprong en schisma. Artikelen over Jezus, het Jodendom en het vroege Christendom.* [Between Origin and Schism. Articles on Jesus, Judaism and early Christianity] Hilversum: B. Folkertsma Stichting for Talmudica.

Flusser, D. (1988). Judaism and the Origins of Christianity. Jerusalem: Magnes Press.

Goodenough, E.R. (1940). An introduction to Philo Judaeus. New Haven: Yale University Press.

Gotlieb, A. (2000). *De droom der rede. Een geschiedenis van de filosfie van de Grieken tot de Renaissance.* Amsterdam: Ambo [The Dream of Reason: A History of Philosophy from the Greeks to the Renaissance. London: The Penguin Press].

Grayzel, S. (1963). A History of the Jews. Philadelphia: The Jewish Publication Society of America.

Johnson, P. (1987). A History of the Jews. New York: Harper and Row.

Küng, H. (1991). *Het Jodendom. Wezen, geschiedenis en toekomst.* Utrecht: Ten Have [(1995) Judaism: Between Today and Tomorrow. London: Bloomsbury Academic].

Levine, A.J. (2006). The Misunderstood Jew. The Church and the Scandal of the Jewish Jesus. New York: Harper One.

Levine, A.J., Brettler, M.Z. (Eds) (2011) The Jewish Annotated New Testament. Oxford: Oxford University Press.

Neusner, J. (2002). Judaism. An introduction. London: Penguin Books.

Neusner, J. Avery-Peck, A.J. (Eds) (2000). The Blackwell Companion to Judaism. Oxford: Blackwell.

Philo (1993). The Works of Philo. Complete and unabridged. (Translated by C.D. Yonge). Hendrickson Publishers.

Riches, J. (1990). The World of Jesus. First-century Judaism in crisis. Cambridge. Cambridge University Press.

Saldarini, A.J. (1988). Pharisees, Scribes and Sadducees in Palestinian Society. Grand Rapids / Cambridge U.K.: William B. Eerdmans Publishing Company.

Sandmel, S. (1979). Philo of Alexandria. An introduction. New York/London: Oxford University Press.

Vermes, G. (2010). Jesus and the Jewish World. London: SCM Press.

Vermes, G. (2012). Christian Beginnings. From Nazareth to Nicea. AD 30–325. London Penguin Books.

INDEX